PRACTICAL SUGGESTIONS FOR TEACHING

Edited by Alice Miel

Common Elements in New Mathematics Programs: Their Origins and Evolution

Common Elements in
New Mathematics
Programs

THEIR ORIGINS AND EVOLUTION

Helene Sherman

QUEENS COLLEGE
THE CITY UNIVERSITY OF NEW YORK

TEACHERS COLLEGE PRESS • NEW YORK AND LONDON

Contents

Foreword

The fundamental decisions in education are about *who* is to teach *what* to *whom*. While emphasis may shift under the impact of current fashion, genuine progress in education always requires balance in consideration of these three aspects.

During the period between the time (1967) when this study was prepared and the time (1972) of its publication, the focus of attention in the American educational world has moved to the struggle over who is to have the decision-making power. Clearly, improvement of the quality of education depends on the decision-makers' understanding of the problems involved in the three basic areas where decisions must be made.

We hope that the present study, coming from a person with extensive experience in teaching teachers, will contribute to a revival of interest in the substance of education.

The author rightly stresses the historical roots of the mathematical ideas which were introduced into the curriculum. The origin of a concept often suggests the important natural problems which led people to invent it, the natural questions to ask about it; and the study of origins emphasizes mathematics as the result of creative activity by human beings like the students we wish to teach. This fits very well with a fundamental common goal of all the new curricular programs: to lead the children to participate actively in the development of the subject they are learning.

The historical approach is not only important for understanding of the subject itself but also for understanding of the educational movement described in this report. The serious national attention to the need for improvement in mathematics and science education began as far back as the Steelman Committee's report to the President in 1948. The activity in mathematics was part of a national movement embracing scholars and educators in all branches of knowledge. (The movement's breadth and depth are reflected in a collection of papers edited by this writer in 1964, *Modern Viewpoints in the Curriculum.*)

The author alludes briefly to the meetings in February, 1958, which converted the efforts of a few pioneers, working in comparative isolation, into a national joint effort of mathematicians and educators to improve the teaching of mathematics in this country. It is difficult to *recapture the excitement* of those days when, for the first time in a century, there seemed to be practical prospects for us to make over, on a significant scale, our portion of the world.

Mathematicians, teacher educators, and schoolmen worked enthusiastically together, exchanging ideas, producing materials, and trying them out in classrooms. The excitement even infected school administrators and parents, who were inspired by the sight of teachers really teaching, and youngsters really learning, important ideas, and enjoying it.

PAUL C. ROSENBLOOM

April 1972

Editor's Preface

In her work with young people preparing to teach and with established teachers and supervisors caught up in a true revolution in the teaching of mathematics, Dr. Sherman has found many of them in need of help. In response she has made a careful analysis of six major mathematics programs developed in the fifties and embodied in curriculum guides and instructional materials in the sixties. The identification of elements common to the programs studied is a useful contribution in itself, for it affords a basis for comparison and for utilizing the strong features of the different programs.

Dr. Sherman's contribution does not, however, end with ordering and clarifying ideas associated with the newer mathematics programs. The enduring value of this book lies in the sound and clear way the author has illuminated the origins of basic mathematical ideas. To be enlightened about the process of development of these ideas not only causes one to stand in awe of some of man's great achievements but also gives one fundamental notions about mathematics that will not soon be outmoded.

This work will be invaluable for those engaged in preservice and inservice teacher education and for the teacher of mathematics at any level—elementary, secondary, or collegiate. It will give the educator that most useful of tools—a better grasp of the subject matter he is responsible for teaching.

ALICE MIEL

Kabul
March 1972

Acknowledgments

My expressions of deepest gratitude and affection go to Alice Miel, who saw in my professional concerns the possibility of systematic study, helped me to shape this effort, and provided the major inspiration and wise counsel that brought it to fruition.

Grateful acknowledgment is due Paul Rosenbloom for generous sharing of his mathematics materials, his thoughtful consultation, and continued interest.

I am very much indebted to my friend and colleague Frances Minor, who first directed my attention to the significance of historical search in curriculum development; to my husband, Murray Sherman, for valuable editorial assistance—his respect for the purpose and content of the study has been a prominent source of encouragement; to my mother, Jeannette Kahan, for life-long interest and support, which has been very influential throughout my career.

Laura Whitehall of Teachers College Press deserves special mention for excellent suggestions and consultation that led to expansion of Chapter Eight, on the structure of number systems, and for the care she has taken in preparing the manuscript for publication.

Finally, I have been deeply moved by the dedication and scholarship of the historians whose works are herein represented.

H. S.

For out of olde feldes, as men seith,
Cometh al this newe corn fro yeer to yere;
And out of olde bokes, in good feith,
Cometh al this newe science that men lere.

—GEOFFREY CHAUCER, *The Parlement of Foules*

Common Elements in
New Mathematics Programs

THEIR ORIGINS AND EVOLUTION

ONE

Introduction

The history of hints given before the time at which they were (perhaps could be) made to bear fruit, would be a very curious one; and the progress of science will never be well understood until some little account can, in each case, be given of the reason why a notion should be so productive at a particular period, which was so barren at a previous one.

—AUGUSTUS DE MORGAN [1] *

The present time is one in which, more than ever before, people are concerned with ordering their information, analyzing and simplifying it so that knowledge may be comprehended in its deepest sense, related to larger complexes of ideas, and used in ways that reflect a grasp of this depth and relatedness.

This book has grown out of the writer's professional interest in these concerns as they pertain to mathematics education. It presents two kinds of information—for teachers, teacher educators, and others responsible for planning mathematics curricula. (Teachers may find that some students and parents will want to read it, too.)

It reviews the development of major new mathematics programs, identifying the most significant elements of their content. And it provides a historical context for key concepts and areas of mathematics, tracing ideas, symbols, and procedures to their origins in ancient times. This treatment includes curriculum material that can aid in the transition from traditional to modern ways of teaching, learning, and enjoying mathematics.

* Numbered Notes are gathered on pages 143–50.

1

The perspective from which the book is written is one that emerged in a curriculum reform movement that began in the mid-fifties and of which "new mathematics" projects were an early and important part. Two ideas basic to that movement were *key concepts* and *structure of a discipline*. Recognition of key concepts in a particular field was viewed as contributing depth and significance to one's understanding of the subject, providing economy in learning, and promoting further independent work.

Mathematicians and other pure scientists have identified such key ideas in their respective disciplines, and the professional literature in education has reflected appreciation of these insights. Ways in which such structuring principles may be implemented at different levels of complexity have also received some attention.[2]

More than fifteen years have gone by since the start of the curriculum reform movement that initiated new mathematics projects. During this period schools across the nation have introduced a variety of new programs, new textbooks, novel methods and materials. And to date, in part because of the multiplicity of these innovations and the experimental nature of many, there is still widespread uncertainty about programs labeled "new mathematics."

Teachers wishing to advance their understanding of the new movement in mathematics need answers to both of these questions: (1) What are the key ideas most commonly emphasized in the major elementary and intermediate programs? (2) How and why have these key concepts developed and achieved their present significance?

The professional literature dealing with the movement has not adequately answered these needs. There do exist several teachers' bulletins designed to clarify what is "new" in new mathematics, to describe some of the new programs, and to explain some of the ideas related to their content and methodology.* These bulletins, however, have little or nothing to say about the significance of the key content elements in terms of their origins and evolution.

Perhaps the most critical problem in the implementation of the new programs has been, and still is, the difficulty teachers have in making the transition from traditional programs to modern ones. The importance of this transition to their students is surely clear. Mathematics has long been viewed as a highly technical subject that only a few are expected to handle competently. But in the present era, with the increased application of mathematics to so many new areas of living, it is essential that the educated person have a working knowledge of mathematics in order to understand his environment.

* See the Appendix for a list of such bulletins.

Teachers, especially those who are products of wholly traditional education programs, need some ways of identifying with and becoming comfortable with mathematics concepts newly introduced at the elementary and intermediate levels. The writer's experience with both students and teachers has emphatically shown that the historical context delineated in this book may be of assistance to all concerned. Becoming aware of, and in a sense re-experiencing, the problems of earlier times that led to the development of today's mathematics may be the link needed to move from a traditional approach to one concerned with significant concepts and the structure of mathematics as a field of knowledge.

Tracing the historical development of mathematics illuminates important social processes in which man has engaged. This value has been recognized by other writers. Spencer and Brydegaard, for example, say: "As a social study mathematics treats not only of devices and procedures with number systems, but it treats of the problems which people experience in trying to understand and to make fitting adjustments with regard for all sorts of experiences with quantity." [3]

As further support for this point, it should be noted that the Cambridge Conference on School Mathematics (1963), which had as its main purpose the preparation of a new framework for mathematics curriculum, from kindergarten through grade twelve, emphasized the cultural value of mathematics as follows: "The historical background of a topic often makes clear the motivation for discussing it. This background stimulates many students by providing the human interest and showing the connection of mathematics with other important events. It is of value in the understanding of the processes of mathematical creativity; *all known mathematics was discovered by somebody.*" [4] (Italics added.)

This view can be extended further to emphasize discernment—in the evolution of mathematics concepts—of certain of civilization's continuing threads and characteristics.

Neither traditional nor new mathematics programs thus far, however, have related the progress of mathematics to broad social and cultural processes. Materials that emphasize key ideas of contemporary programs and their gradual development over the centuries should therefore be of considerable value in teacher education. This book comprises such material, intended to put key mathematical ideas into an enlightening perspective that provides for broad understanding and applicability.

Part I presents discussion of the curriculum reform context of the new mathematics movement, an overview of the movement itself, descriptions of six major new programs, and an analysis of these programs with respect to what is common among them. Six key concept areas are found to be given generally comprehensive treatment in the over-all curriculum of all or most of the programs: (1) numeration systems, (2) measurement, (3) geometric ideas, (4) algebraic ideas, (5) structure (laws and systems), and (6) sets.

Part II relates basic information about content in each of these areas to a detailed historical context. The role of human ingenuity in creating and developing important concepts, notations, and applications is stressed, as are the environmental and social conditions that affected their evolution.

In this perspective which views mathematics as one strand in the thread of human development from primitive times to the present, certain continuing characteristics in the cultural life of man, including his proneness to change and evolution, may be discerned. These ought not to be overlooked in teaching young people:

1. There is a relationship between what has been and what is. Recognition of such relationships is fundamental to understanding and appreciating any part of our present environment.

2. Not all historical sources are in agreement. There are uncertainties, errors, injustices. In the end one must often consider the differences and similarities in sources, weigh them carefully, and decide for oneself.

3. Change does not necessarily imply progress. There have been instances in history of backward steps, and this possibility is ever present.

4. Through the ages, man has constantly sought to increase precision in measurement and to improve symbolic notation. He will continue to do so.

5. The symbols people select to stand for given ideas are largely arbitrary choices. The nature of a particular selection may facilitate or hamper progress.

6. Language and symbolic notation have undergone many changes over the centuries and will continue to change.

7. Uniformity in mathematics symbolism is essential to accurate scientific communication among people and nations. At the present time, future improvements seem to lie in the direction of international cooperation.

8. Some of the fundamental mathematical observations that seem simplest or most self-evident today were overlooked by the most gifted scholars of ancient times and later centuries. Future generations may wonder at the apparent blindness of scholars of the present era.

9. There are usually different and equally valid modes in which a given problem can be conceptualized.

10. The most eminent scholars may fail to recognize the value of a new idea because they are unable to depart from habitual patterns of thinking.

11. Even when a problem is generally recognized, it often takes many years to resolve it.

12. The preoccupations, inclinations, aversions, and superstitions of a given culture will have a profound effect upon the nature of its achievements.

13. People have always been deeply interested in and affected by the thinking of those who preceded them.

14. Society's present cultural level has resulted from the accumulated and integrated knowledge and experience of the past.

15. Each field of knowledge has developed out of the need of human beings to cope with challenging situations in their environment.

16. An interest in one aspect of a particular field has often led to the development of advanced ideas in rather remote aspects of that field as well as other fields.

Mathematics in particular, like subject matter in general, provides ways of organizing knowledge, tools for coping with the environment, aids to understanding the physical world. Subject matter fields are bodies of knowledge which are active and growing, and which man continually shapes and reshapes to meet the problems arising from change.

By tracing the path of certain mathematical concepts and their progress through the works of centuries gone by, present knowledge of these concepts may be comprehended in a deeper sense, both as part of the field itself and as it relates to other fields and to social processes. It is hoped that the material presented in this book, about ideas and applications in basic areas emphasized in new programs, will help to fill an important gap in the present treatment of mathematics curriculum.

Part I

NEW MATHEMATICS

The Movement and the Programs

The twentieth century has been the golden age of mathematics, since more mathematics, and more profound mathematics has been created in this period than all the rest of history. . . .

—NCTM [1]

During the 1950's, in order to meet national needs and problems of expanding knowledge, mathematics scholars in several parts of the country joined with educational specialists to develop appropriate new mathematics programs for elementary and secondary schools. Most of these programs were made available for general use within a relatively short period, roughly from 1957 to 1959. All at once they seemed to become the center of attention, and no one who was responsible for the mathematics education of young people could easily ignore their existence.

A number of professional bulletins contain descriptions of the different mathematics projects, together with comments on their growth. This book does not attempt to deal in depth with the new mathematics movement. A brief overview of its background and development is provided in Chapter Two, however, for the purpose of contributing to the total picture as it relates to particular concerns of this book. In Chapter Three, six major new programs are described in terms of their stated objectives, the range and availability of their teaching materials, and their common features of content and methodology.

TWO

The Movement

AN OVERVIEW

THE CURRICULUM REFORM CONTEXT

In American education, a major emphasis of the fifties and sixties was centered on the disciplines as a source of curriculum content. At a 1961 conference sponsored by the Department of Curriculum and Teaching, Teachers College, Columbia University, Philip Phenix said:

> . . . authentic disciplines are at one and the same time approximations to the given orders of reality and disclosures of the paths by which persons may come to realize truth in their own being; which is simply to say that the disciplines are the sole proper source of the curriculum.[1]

This emphasis grew in part out of the concern of educators for dealing with the rapid expansion of information in almost all fields of knowledge. Also, competition with Communist countries placed unprecedented pressure upon our schools to produce a large number of highly qualified mathematicians, engineers, and scientists.

It was primarily these scientific and technological demands, along with the educational problems inherent in a knowledge explosion, which led to a unified effort to discover more effective ways of teaching and learning.

One idea which emerged as a means of meeting this challenge was that of identifying essential elements in the fields of knowledge as a basis for curriculum content. This notion has been particularly evident since the appearance in 1956 of an essay entitled "Key Concepts and the Crisis in Learning," also by Phenix, in which he said:

> . . . the theory of knowledge in its several areas provides a means for developing key concepts which by indicating the essential character of

9

whole fields of knowledge can insure the necessary general understanding with relatively limited knowledge of specific details. The use of such key ideas in the organization and teaching of subject matter may effect important economies in learning effort, greatly increase the depth of comprehension, and facilitate further independent exploration in any discipline.[2]

Later, in *Philosophy of Education* (1958), Phenix expanded a philosophical analysis of the fields of knowledge which he felt would "help to provide understanding of their *essential* features, and thus enable the teacher to place emphasis on central and definitive matters rather than on a host of subordinate details, the relevance of which may not be clear to the student." [3]

The participation of university scholars in curriculum development has constituted a significant and still growing trend, one that has distinctly narrowed the gap between scholarship and its application to educational process. From one such group effort, the Woods Hole Conference at Cape Cod, Massachusetts, September 1959, came another view which had a striking impact on the field of education. Jerome Bruner, writing about structure as the fundamental element in learning subject matter, said:

Grasping the structure of a subject is understanding it in a way that permits many other things to be related to it meaningfully. To learn structure, in short, is to learn how things are related.[4]

And also:

To understand something as a specific instance of a more general case—which is what understanding a more fundamental principle or structure means—is to have learned not only a specific thing but also a model for understanding other things like it that one may encounter.[5]

The ideas of key concepts and structure became the foundation of curriculum development programs of the early 1960's, and since that time the thinking of academicians and educational specialists, as well as the work in curriculum revision, has reflected this emphasis.

THE REVOLUTION IN MATHEMATICS

"The changes in mathematics in progress at the present time are so extensive, so far-reaching in their implications, and so profound that they can be described only as a revolution." Thus said the authors of *The Revolution in School Mathematics,* a report of Regional Orientation Conferences in Mathematics of the National Council of Teachers of Mathematics (NCTM), in 1961.

The report cites three major causes of this revolution: research in mathematics; automation; and the introduction of high-speed electronic computing machines. With reference to research in mathematics, the Council says this:

> The twentieth century has been the golden age of mathematics, since more mathematics, and more profound mathematics has been created in this period than all the rest of history. . . . The present century has seen the introduction and extensive development of subjects in pure mathematics such as abstract algebra, topology, measure theory, general theories of integration, and functional analysis. . . . There has been rapid development in certain other fields of mathematics which are more closely related to important applications than those already named. Probability and statistics are studied not only for their own sake, but also because of their extensive and important applications in the physical and engineering sciences, in the biological sciences, and in the social sciences.[6]

Also mentioned in connection with research is the theory of games, dating from 1944, "a mathematical model in terms of which economic forces and behavior could be explained and understood," and linear programing, dating from 1948, "a tool for the more efficient management of large-scale industrial and government operations."[7]

The automation revolution is defined by the Council as the introduction of machines that control machines, and the consequence of the use of such machines. Long distance telephone dialing, automatic pilot control, and guided missiles are examples given. "Not only has it [the automation revolution] created the necessity for solving complicated design and development problems, but it has contributed an important tool for their solution."[8] This tool, the automatic digital computing machine, is listed as the third cause of the revolution in mathematics:

> This computer has made it possible for mathematical theory to be teamed with the computing machine to produce answers that are required by physicists, engineers, and others. . . . The importance of the electronic digital computing machine arises not from the fact that certain calculations can be carried out more quickly than heretofore, but rather from the fact that computations which were formerly completely impossible can now be made quickly and efficiently.[9]

An illustration of this point is the flight of a guided missile for which a computer makes the required calculations and directs the missile through radar connections in a matter of seconds.

The technological revolution has required a careful analysis of the mathematics content of courses at each educational level; it has required the development of mathematics programs which include topics related to present needs as well as to those needs projected for the future; it has required improved teaching-learning processes.

A report on curriculum studies in academic subjects sponsored by the National Education Association describes the mathematics curriculum before the development of new programs in this way:

> Until recently, the mathematics curriculum in elementary and secondary schools had been relatively unchanged for a century or more. It had been generally uniform across the nation. For the most part, the sequence of topics and their grade placement was determined by tradition rather than by efforts to discover what could be learned most effectively by children at various age levels, although experimental studies of the 1930's had some influence on the elementary-school sequence. Mathematical principles and concepts developed over the last half of a century were treated briefly, or not at all, in the school curriculum.[10]

It is generally acknowledged that traditional mathematics programs emphasize memorization, drill, speed in calculating, and the use of prescribed formulas rather than thinking, reasoning, and understanding computational operations—characteristics currently recognized as having priority. At the present time there is evidence nationally of rather wide interest and acceptance of new emphases in mathematics education. But whereas there has been considerable progress in the development and implementation of mathematics curriculum proposals to suit a contemporary society, few educators would deny that there remains much to be accomplished before mathematics curricula rest on solid ground. Among the challenges to be met are improvement of the mathematics preparation of teachers and more effective communication and interaction between those responsible for developing curricula and those responsible for teaching children and youth.

THE MATHEMATICS CURRICULUM PROJECTS

The beginning of the curriculum reform movement in mathematics is commonly associated with the work of the University of Illinois Committee on School Mathematics in 1951. This UICSM project, concerned with problems of high school mathematics, initially addressed itself to the question of whether able mathematicians and teachers working together could develop instructional materials, prepare teachers in their use, and produce students who understand and have interest in mathematics. The project represented the joint effort of the College of Education, the College of Engineering, and the College of Liberal Arts and Sciences at the University of Illinois. The program emphasizes the structure of mathematics, learning mathematical principles through discovery, consistency, and precise terminology.

The numerous projects that have been developed and widely used since 1951 are a matter of record. They represent an extensive effort to improve mathematics curriculum at levels ranging from kindergarten through college, including teacher education programs, both pre-service and inservice.

The earliest of these efforts, UICSM and the Boston College Mathematics Institute (BCMI), started with an interest in mathematics curricula at the college level. Both groups soon realized that college freshmen lacked modern mathematics background and that it was the secondary school curriculum to which their attention must first be given.

In another instance, the Chicago Conference on Research Potential and Training (February 21, 1958), sponsored by the National Science Foundation (NSF), recognized that the shortage of research mathematicians in graduate and postgraduate programs was caused, at least in part, by inadequate instruction in the early school years. A major recommendation of this conference was that the American Mathematical Society (AMS) appoint a committee of mathematicians to work toward a solution of the existing mathematics curriculum problem.

At the Mathematics Meeting of the NSF held a week later (February 28, 1958), at the Massachusetts Institute of Technology, the membership included not only mathematicians but also physicists from the Physical Science Study Commission who had two years of experience working on school curriculum development. Also seriously concerned with the state of mathematics curricula in American schools, this conference endorsed the recommendation made at the Chicago meeting and specified that a committee be appointed to develop a syllabus for a model mathematics curriculum, grades seven through twelve.

It was out of these two conferences and to meet the responsibility of developing a model curriculum that the School Mathematics Study Group (SMSG) was established by the AMS-appointed Committee of Eight.

William Wooton, in *SMSG: The Making of a Curriculum*, notes that the importance of AMS approval of such a committee cannot be over-stated:

> An organization composed entirely of mathematicians, it is the senior (in both age and sophistication of interests) of all of the professional organizations of mathematicians in the United States, and, consequently, it maintains just that degree of disinterest toward the ordinary affairs of mankind that it feels necessary to the protection of its chosen function, research in mathematics.
>
> . . . . .
>
> For more than thirty years, the AMS had held itself aloof from the elementary and secondary school level of mathematics and had con-

tributed very little to the teaching of it. With the appointment of the Committee of Eight, it officially expressed an interest in the mathematics curriculum of the schools, and the approval of the Society made it possible for a large number of distinguished college teachers and research mathematicians to enter wholeheartedly into cooperation with high school teachers in a concerted effort to improve the quality and presentation of school mathematics.[11]

Although the appointed committee was not a committee of the AMS, or responsible to it, Wooton adds, "The act of appointment gave clear indication that the long estrangement between research mathematicians and teachers of mathematics had been breached."

SMSG has become the largest effort in mathematics curriculum improvement to date. National in scope, it represents the combined thinking of prominent scholars in the field of mathematics, experienced teachers and supervisors in mathematics education, and representatives from both professional and industrial organizations involved in highly significant scientific research.

At about the same time as SMSG was getting started, several other groups in different locations throughout the country also focused on the central problems of teaching mathematics to young people. A whole new mathematics movement was emerging.

In 1957 the University of Maryland Mathematics Project (UMMaP) was developing its program for grades seven and eight as a cooperative endeavor of four local public school systems and the university departments of mathematics, education, psychology, and engineering. Fundamental learning processes, as these relate to mathematics education, soon became a major interest of this group.

An experimental project in the teaching of elementary school mathematics was taking root at Stanford University in 1959; it was based on the assumption that young children could learn much more than educators had previously thought possible and on Suppes' premise that "all mathematics can be developed from the concept of set and operations upon set." [12]

The research of Muller-Willis and Rosenbloom on mathematics concepts and young children was providing, in part, the basis for a University of Minnesota program (begun in 1958) which had two main emphases: the geometrical model of the real number system as a means of developing mathematical understanding and furthering application of learnings, and the use of problems related to the natural and social sciences as well as to other fields of knowledge. This program is usually referred to by the acronym MINNEMAST, for Minnesota Mathematics and Science Teaching Project.

Interested in making mathematics an exciting adventure for children,

David Page, at the University of Illinois, in 1958, was exploring different ways of approaching familiar topics, adapting advanced topics for earlier use, and developing mathematical frameworks which would provide a focus for ideas. He encouraged children to guess, to invent, to try things out. The work of the project (not to be confused with the UICSM program of 1951) has stressed intuitive thinking through which children grasp the essence of mathematics.

A 1957 conference between the principal of Madison Junior High School in Syracuse, New York, and Robert B. Davis of Syracuse University led in the same year to the formation of the Madison Project, as it has come to be called. Interested in revitalizing the mathematics program at this junior high school, Davis started his work with seventh graders and subsequently shifted to lower and lower grade levels. Essentially an enrichment program with subject matter adapted to the maturity of the children, the Madison Project is characterized by instruction through questioning, early introduction to basic concepts, maximum student participation, and emphasis on intuitive algebraic and geometric ideas.

And the Greater Cleveland Mathematics Program (GCMP) was soon to start working (in 1959) "to develop a comprehensive, sequential mathematics program for *all* children in grades kindergarten through twelve, a program which is both mathematically correct and pedagogically sound." [13]

The foregoing survey refers to most, though not all, of the experimental programs initiated during the 1950's.* This material has been presented in order to provide a general picture of mathematics curriculum development by various groups since 1950. Table 1 gives the information in condensed form.

Over the years, program names have been changed, as have directors and addresses. The most recent information available from the individual projects in the spring of 1967 was used in the preparation of Table 1 as well as in preparing this developmental sketch. The listing of several sources as financial sponsors indicates that each has con-

* The Nuffield Mathematics Teaching Project, developed in England during the mid-sixties, has been deemed by Robert Davis "one of the finest and most carefully devised of all of the 'modern mathematics' projects." Based partly on Piaget's studies of developmental stages in child growth, the project focuses on experiences working with physical materials and is individualized for each child. Materials are prepared for teachers (not children). They are available from: The Nuffield Foundation, Mathematics Teaching Project, 12 Upper Belgrave Street, London, S.W. 1, England. For a more detailed description of the project, see Robert Davis, *The Changing Curriculum: Mathematics* (1967), pp. 26-39.

TABLE 1

OVERVIEW OF THE DEVELOPMENT OF MATHEMATICS PROGRAMS SINCE 1951[a]

Program	Year Started	Present[b] Range	Director & Address	Support[c]	Essentials
University of Illinois Committee on School Mathematics	1951	Secondary Grades 7, 8	Max Beberman UICSM Mathematics Project 1210 West Springfield Urbana, Illinois 61801	Univ. of Illinois USOE NSF Carnegie	Logical structure of mathematics; study of patterns Consistency; precise terminology Learning through discovery Early verbalization discouraged Non-graded units to be used in accordance with student background and experience
Boston College Mathematics Institute	(1953)[d] 1957	College Secondary Elementary	Stanley J. Bezuska, S.J. BCMI Department of Mathematics Boston College Chestnut Hill Massachusetts 02167	NSF	Structure of mathematics from the historical point of view Cultural aspects of man's experience with numbers Precise terminology Correspondence course with graduate credit for teachers
Ball State University	1955	Secondary Elementary	Robert E. Eicholz Ball State University Experimental Mathematics Project Muncie, Indiana 47306	Ball State Univ.	Structure of mathematics Interrelatedness of principles Logical development Deemphasis on social arithmetic Stress on mathematical ideas Intuitive and axiomatic approaches
Madison Project	1957	Secondary Elementary	Robert B. Davis The Madison Project 918 Irving Avenue Syracuse, N.Y. 13210	NSF USOE	Discovery of structure through finding one's own solutions to problems Discussion through careful questioning Unstructured tasks; social applications deliberately omitted Ungraded material intended as a supplementary program Integration of arithmetic, algebra, and geometry
University of Maryland Mathematics Project	1959	Grades 7, 8 Elementary	John R. Mayor, UMMaP College of Education College Park Maryland 20740	Carnegie NSF Funds from sale of texts	Mathematics as a language; precise terminology Properties of a mathematical structure Unifying concepts; particular emphasis on number systems Learning through discovery Inductive and deductive reasoning Verbal and operational components simultaneously encouraged Fundamental learning processes a major concern of the project

Project	Year	Level	Director / Institution	Support[c]	Characteristics[a][b]
Stanford University Sets and Numbers Project	1959	Elementary	Patrick Suppes, Experimental Teaching of Mathematics in the Elementary School, Stanford University, Stanford, California 94305	Carnegie NSF USOE	Concept of set and operations on set; Precise language; mathematical laws; Logic; Relationship between set theory and foundations of arithmetic; Algebraic and geometric principles
School Mathematics Study Group	1958	Secondary Elementary	E. G. Begle, SMSG, Stanford University, Stanford, California 94305	NSF	Structure of mathematics; Concepts of mathematics as part of the whole of mathematics not just to some sub-division; Spiral approach; New content as well as conventional topics; opportunity for conventional practice and review; No strong position on verbal-operational question
Arithmetic[e] Project	[d]1958	Elementary	David A. Page, Arithmetic Project, Educational Services Incorporated, 108 Water Street, Watertown, Massachusetts, 02172	Univ. of Illinois Carnegie NSF	Mathematical exploration; Topics with "travel" – an adventure; Intuitive thinking: guessing; inventing; trying things out; Developing a feeling for mathematical ideas; No stress on verbalization; not a complete course of study; no grade levels; Project seeks teachable alternatives for important mathematical ideas
Greater Cleveland Mathematics Program	1959	Secondary Elementary	George Cunningham, Educational Research Council of Greater Cleveland, 614 W. Superior Ave. Cleveland, Ohio 44113	The Council	Logical structure of mathematics; Mathematical laws; Discovery approach; Search for patterns and relationships; Emphasis on a continuous and systematic flow of mathematics concept formation K-12
Minnesota Mathematics and Science Teaching Project	(1958)[f] 1961	Elementary	James H. Wentz, Jr., MINNEMAST, Project Director, University of Minnesota, Minneapolis, Minnesota 55455; Paul C. Rosenbloom[g], MINNEMAST, Mathematics Director, Teachers College, Columbia University, New York, N.Y. 10027	NSF	Three specific mathematics structures: the real number system, Euclidean space, a space with measure; Concepts of an algebraic structure and a deductive science; Connections between mathematics and science; cultural and historical aspects of mathematics; Working toward a coordinated mathematics-science curriculum K-9 and undergraduate courses for pre-service education of teachers; Ungraded units

[a] Based primarily on reports and brochures of the individual projects, available in January 1967.
[b] Program materials may be available for students only, for teachers only, or for both.
[c] Abbreviations: USOE for United States Office of Education; NSF for National Science Foundation; Carnegie for Carnegie Corp.
[d] Started informally in 1953.   [e] Formerly the University of Illinois Arithmetic Project.   [g] Project director 1961-1966.
[f] Grew out of the MINNEMATH program which started in 1958.

tributed at some time, but does not mean that all of these sponsors are necessarily contributing funds at the present time.

The projects are intended primarily for *all* students. In a few instances certain materials of a particular project are intended either for students capable of advancing quickly or for students who have special instructional needs. Since this specialized aspect of new programs does not relate directly to the present investigation, further discussion of this feature is omitted.

In concluding this account of the development of recently initiated mathematics curriculum proposals, the following two points are worthy of note: (1) There has been strong affirmation of the importance of quality instruction in the early school years, with corresponding attention in many projects to elementary mathematics education programs. (2) There has been wide recognition that advances in teacher education must parallel advances in mathematics education for children, with corresponding attention to publications for teachers, workshops, and special institutes.

THREE

Six Programs

THEIR COMMON FEATURES

This study of common elements in new mathematics programs is based in part on detailed analysis of six major programs, selected after a general survey of the various existing programs. The choice was made to be both representative and complete in terms of the points of view and approaches which have been offered regarding curriculum and teaching of mathematics in the elementary school. These were the six programs selected:

The Ball State University Experimental Mathematics Project
The Greater Cleveland Mathematics Program
The Madison Project
The Minnesota Mathematics and Science Teaching Project
The School Mathematics Study Group Program
The Stanford University Sets and Numbers Program

The choice of these programs is based on several criteria of selection. In general, the programs are those in widest use in terms of currency and distribution. Through acknowledgment and description in curriculum bulletins and professional journals, and through actual use in the classroom, the programs have achieved national prominence. In addition, three more specific criteria are used: (1) the programs are intended as kindergarten-through-sixth-grade sequential curricula; (2) the program materials are intended for direct use by children, and (3) the programs as a group represent some significant differences among themselves in new approaches to problems in mathematics curriculum in the elementary school.

In the light of these criteria the programs selected do represent a total population: that is, there was at the time of selection no other group of six major programs which met the criteria. Actually, not all of these six meet *each* of the criteria. For example, at present the MINNEMAST program extends only from kindergarten to third grade, and the Madison Project is a supplementary and ungraded program.

The programs as a group do comprise significant variations of approach. The MINNEMAST program is attempting to relate mathematics to science—a feature which distinguishes it from the other five. The Madison Project is specifically oriented toward the learning of algebra and the use of symbols, as the other five programs are not. The SMSG, Stanford, GCMP, and Ball State programs are all oriented toward the use of "set" concepts, a feature not characteristic of the MINNEMAST and Madison programs.

Two of the criteria extend to all six programs. That is, all of them are generally known and in use, and all materials are intended for use by children under the guidance of the teacher.

There are other programs in use which do not meet the selection criteria used here (see Chapter Two and Table 1 for general information on recently developed programs.) Nevertheless, the common elements extracted from the six programs selected for this investigation are also, essentially, the signicant features of the other programs. It is, of course, conceivable and even to be hoped that new programs will be formulated and new discoveries made in the field of mathematics which will introduce elements not treated in this research. However, in the present state of development of mathematics programs for kindergarten through sixth grade, these four criteria of selection serve to identify the most significant and widely used programs, which in turn include the most crucial elements in the field of mathematics study.

SIX PROGRAMS DESCRIBED

In this section, each of the six programs is briefly described in terms of its major objectives, its particular emphases, and the range and availability of its materials at the time of writing.

The Ball State University
Experimental Mathematics Project

The Ball State program was begun in 1955 in an effort to improve material for secondary geometry. Since that time the project has expanded to include new mathematics material for a 7–12 curriculum. The publishers of the 7–12 program later asked the writers to prepare materials for K–6. Although the K–6 series is not officially part of the Ball State program, as an extension of it by the same writers, it is helpful to refer to it that way in this book.

The project's primary purpose (as stated in a mimeographed paper) was "to develop material that will be correct, continuous and so presented to the student that the structure of mathematics is evident."

In contrast to the other programs, the Ball State mathematics program has not received foundation support. The university and the writing team assumed total financial responsibility for preparation of the 7–12 materials and have also sponsored inservice courses and consultant services to schools.

The Ball State program emphasizes the structure of mathematics; major attention is given to the interrelationships of principles; fundamental to this curriculum is the concept of "set." The project authors acknowledge the assistance of the Educational Research Council of Greater Cleveland and the School Mathematics Study Group.

Materials for K–12 are available through Addison-Wesley Publishing Company, South Street, Reading, Massachusetts 01867.

The Greater Cleveland Mathematics Program (GCMP)

The Educational Research Council of Greater Cleveland, a nonprofit, independent organization "dedicated to the task of providing for every child the best possible elementary and secondary school education," [1] responded to the request of its Advisory Committee on Educational Policy (in 1959) to improve the K–12 mathematics curriculum. As a result the Greater Cleveland Mathematics Program was developed.

The program's stated purpose was "to develop a new elementary and secondary mathematics curriculum which can be presented in a logical, articulated and sequential manner" in order to achieve the following major objectives: (1) "the traditional program's sole objective—to develop skillful and rapid computation at the elementary school level and to develop skillful and accurate manipulation of algebraic expressions at the secondary level," and (2) to help the child to discover for himself basic principles that enable him to recognize mathematical structure and thus solve related problems. [2]

Major emphases of this program include: discovery approach, patterns and relationships, and the logical structure of mathematics. Conventional topics are treated, as well as most of the topics identified with new mathematics programs. The program is oriented toward concept formation and adheres to a basic "set" approach.

Materials for K–6 are currently available from Science Research Associates, Inc., 259 Erie Street, Chicago, Illinois 60611.

The Madison Project

The Madison Project is sometimes referred to as the Syracuse University–Webster College Madison Project. Its director, Robert B. Davis, reports that the success of the project's first experimental classroom work (1957) at the Madison School in Syracuse, New York, provided the impetus for further exploration in the teaching and learning of mathematics. Through individualized instruction, seventh-grade children of low IQ, labeled "culturally deprived," learned concepts of algebra and analytic geometry as well as the arithmetic required in these two areas. This success led the project to expand its interest to consider ways of working with both "average" and "gifted" children.[3]

As mentioned earlier, the Madison Project materials constitute a supplementary program. Among its objectives, as stated in a general description of the project,[4] the broadest is "to use mathematics as an approach to the task of improving the quality of precollege education, particularly in relation to giving students a deeper sense of *involvement* in the process of their own education, and to increasing the sense of *vitality* and *relevance* to educational experiences." Objectives related specifically to curriculum are (1) "to *broaden* the curriculum" to include the relationship of arithmetic to algebra and coordinate geometry, (2) "to instill a *more creative flavor* into the school mathematics curriculum," and (3) "to achieve greater *variety* in the children's experiences with mathematics, and more active student participation." Very clear objectives for students and for teachers are also outlined; in particular, the project aims to help teachers of mathematics "to gain an ever deeper understanding of children, and of mathematics, and of the human condition in the twentieth century."

Several working hypotheses of the project are worthy of note:[5] (1) In general, "considerable *experience* with basic concepts and techniques should precede any *formal* instruction." (2) The ability "to discover patterns in abstract material" is one of the most essential mathematical skills. (3) Content and method are equally important and inseparable.

The program stresses unstructured tasks, the discovery of structure through finding one's own solution to problems, discussion through carefully sequenced questioning, and the simultaneous teaching of arithmetic, algebra, and geometry.

Some currently available materials may be obtained from the Madison Project, 918 Irving Avenue, Syracuse, New York 13210; other materials are published commercially by Addison-Wesley Publishing Company, South Street, Reading, Massachusetts 08167. Houghton Mifflin Company is preparing some new inservice materials.

The Minnesota Mathematics and Science Teaching Project (MINNEMAST)

The main ideas for the MINNEMAST program were outlined in December 1959, by Paul Rosenbloom, at a symposium of the Frontiers of Science Foundation of Oklahoma.[6] Starting on a small scale in 1961, aided by a National Science Foundation grant to the School Mathematics Study Group, the work of this project has continued and expanded under NSF support given directly to the University of Minnesota since 1962.

The MINNEMAST project aimed at producing "a coordinated science and mathematics curriculum for grades K–9, together with an experimental pre-service education program for teachers." A basic goal was "to find out what children can learn and then prepare teachers to teach it." [7]

Three specific mathematical structures constitute the program's major focus in subject matter: (1) the real number system (the number line, operations and properties of addition, subtraction, multiplication, division, the coordinate system); (2) Euclidean space (the conceptualization of space in an abstract sense); and (3) a space with measure (the conceptualization of space for concrete applications, as for area and volume). Concepts of an algebraic or rational structure and a deductive science are also prominent ideas in the material developed so far. Arithmetic is illustrated geometrically, and the unification of arithmetic, algebra, and geometry is stressed.

Materials are currently available for K–3 coordinated mathematics and science from MINNEMAST Project, University of Minnesota, 720 Washington Avenue S.E., Minneapolis, Minnesota 55414.

The School Mathematics Study Group (SMSG)

As noted earlier, the SMSG grew out of the recommendations of two 1958 conferences sponsored by the National Science Foundation and was the work of a committee appointed subsequently by the American Mathematical Society.

The primary purpose of SMSG, as stated in the program's bylaws, is "to foster research and development in the teaching of school mathematics." [8] In connection with its general objective of improving mathematics teaching in the schools, SMSG attempts specifically (1) to offer students "not only the basic mathematical skills but also a deeper understanding of the basic concepts and structure of mathematics," (2) to "attract and train more of those students who are capable of studying mathematics with profit," and (3) to provide needed assistance for teachers who are preparing to teach mathematics.[9]

Generally considered conservative, the SMSG program includes both traditional and new content, attempting a fusion of old and new. Conventional content is approached in new ways, but there is considerable opportunity for practice and drill. The structure of mathematics, the concept of "set," and a spiral approach are the program's basic characteristics.

Materials for K–12 are available from Vromans California School Book Depository, 2085 East Foothill Boulevard, Pasadena, Calif. 91109.

The Stanford University
Sets and Numbers Project

The Sets and Numbers Project in Elementary School Mathematics is one of four experimental studies initiated at Stanford University between 1958 and 1964. The other studies are: Geometry for Primary Grades; Mathematical Logic for the School Project, intended for able fifth- and sixth-grade students; and Computer-Based Mathematics Instruction, which programs the materials of the three aforementioned projects for children's use in specially equipped laboratories.

The major objective of the Sets and Numbers Project is "to develop and test a new mathematics curriculum for kindergarten through grade six." [10] The program stresses concepts, laws, and skills of arithmetic but also includes content from other branches of mathematics. The concept of "set" is the foundational and unifying idea upon which the series is based. Particular attention is given to sequence in concept development, the attempt being to move from the concrete to the abstract through several levels of abstraction.

Materials for K–6 are currently available from the L. W. Singer Company, Inc., 249–259 West Erie Boulevard, Syracuse, New York 13201.

COMMON FEATURES OF THE PROGRAMS

Each of the six programs was examined to determine its major emphases, with respect to content and to methods of teaching, and the grade levels at which the various content areas are studied. The results are reported here. The investigation focused on identifying those concepts which characterize new programs; topics which are part of every elementary mathematics curriculum (such as fractions, decimals, percentages, and the basic operations of arithmetic) were not so identified, and they are considered in Part II only as they relate to the content elements selected for detailed treament there.

Common Content Elements

The examination of the programs indicated that certain content elements which were formerly studied at more advanced grade levels are now being introduced in the elementary grades. These include the following ten:

1. Numeration systems
2. Measurement
3. Geometric ideas
4. Algebraic ideas
5. Structure (laws & systems)
6. Sets
7. Statistics
8. Probability
9. Number theory
10. Logic

This list is the result of a comprehensive analysis of the six programs examined, but it is conceivable that another analysis could produce additional elements.

Attention was also given to determining how many of the six programs dealt with each particular concept area and how extensively. Table 2 shows these findings.

Table 2

Grade Levels at which Six New Mathematics Programs Deal with Content Recently Introduced into Elementary Curriculum [a]

Content	Ball State	Stanford	SMSG	GCMP	MINNE-MAST	Madison
Numeration systems	5, 6	3, 5, 6	3–5		2	
Measurement	1–6	3–6	1–6	1–6	K, 2–4	√
Structure (laws and systems)	1–6	3–6	1–6	1–6	1–3	√
Geometric ideas	3–6	1–6	K–6	K, 4–6	K–3	√
Algebraic ideas	2–6	1–6	1–6		2–4	√
Sets	K–6	1–6	K–6	K–6	K, 1, 3	
Number theory	2–6				1, 2	
Logic		3–6				√
Statistics			6	4,6		
Probability		4–6			3	

[a] Based on materials available in 1967.

A recent examination (1972) shows that, except for *numeration systems*, the *first six content areas* listed are now K–6 or 1–6 in all six programs, with these exceptions: MINNEMAST is K–3 or 1–3; Stanford treats *measurement* and *structure* in 2–6; the ungraded Madison program remains unchanged. Beginning *number theory* is now treated extensively in most of the programs. Ball State (now Addison-Wesley Program) has added *logic* for K–6 and *probability* for grade 6. MINNEMAST has added *statistics* for grade 3, material on cultural-historical aspects of mathematics, and recommendations for transition to other science and mathematics materials in the intermediate grades.

The Madison Project was planned to supplement any good mathematics curriculum. There are no graded materials. Therefore only a check mark is used in Table 2 to indicate the inclusion of a content area in that program.

It should be recalled that four of the programs—Ball State, Stanford, SMSG, and GCMP—have graded material for K–6.

MINNEMAST, which is working toward the development of a sequential K–9 mathematics–science curriculum, had at the time of this analysis 23 mathematics units (Unit 10 was deleted from the original program) and 10 science units. These were ungraded, but the following grade distribution was recommended for the mathematics units by the MINNEMAST staff: kindergarten, Units 1–4; first grade, Units 5–9; second grade, Units 11–15; third grade, Units 16–19; fourth grade, Units 20–24. At this writing, MINNEMAST consists of a K–3 coordinated mathematics and science program, the separate K–4 mathematics and K–2 science having been rendered obsolete.

Table 2 further illustrates that of the ten content areas identified as characteristic elements of new programs, six are given generally comprehensive attention in the over-all elementary curriculum: numeration systems, measurement, geometric ideas, algebraic ideas, structure (laws and systems), and sets. It is basic concepts in these areas that are the "common elements"—the "key concepts"—with which this book is concerned.

Commonalities of Method

It is generally recognized that with new emphases in mathematics content there have been concomitant changes in methods of teaching. Although attention to this aspect of new programs is in many ways as important as the content itself, only partial consideration of such a complex matter can be undertaken here.

With few exceptions commonalities of method in new mathematics programs are not explicitly written into the programs. One is more likely to learn about these from reading the related current literature prepared by mathematicians and educators connected with developing and implementing programs.

In general, the programs themselves tend to place the responsibility for creative methodology with the classroom teacher. For example, in each of the Stanford *Sets and Numbers* texts, teachers are "encouraged to determine the methods and procedures most desirable" for their students. Ball State and GCMP call upon the teacher for an approach which encourages children to search for new patterns and ideas and to find relationships among them. Whereas the emphasis in these programs is on mathematical ideas rather than on mechanics and memorization, the texts in most ways still follow a conventional style: explanation of a particular principle, followed by directions for working out a series of problems, each requiring one correct answer. Typical of suggestions to teachers are such directions as the following:

Call attention to . . .

Tell the children that . . .

Ask the children how many . . .

Have the children identify . . .

Instruct the children to . . .

Direct the children in completing . . .

These are typical directions and questions for children:

Find each sum.

Copy and complete each problem.

Which sets are finite?

What number?

Which is farther?

SMSG, in its *Mathematics for the Elementary School* texts, also follows the explanation–directions–exercises pattern. There is, however, an interesting variation in its approach to this traditional format. The writing is characterized by a conversational quality and an invitation to think about things rather than to accept what is presented. The following excerpts illustrate:

This seems to be a good way for us to . . .

What is the easiest way for us to think about . . .

Imagine that you have . . .

And (from the text for grade 4, pages 53, 54):

First consider the idea of order as it relates to whole numbers associated with sets of things . . .

Now consider the idea of order as it relates to numbers represented by points on a number line.

Exercises which provide for some individuality in thinking and response include such directions as:

Use some different ways to complete each of these statements.

Write a question that . . .

MINNEMAST deals with important mathematical ideas in story context suited to children's interests. For example, the idea of sets is introduced through a story about a youngster whose toys are strewn all over the house. The process of putting his things in order lends itself to consideration of sets of airplanes, sets of trucks, and so forth. Worksheets are part of each unit and, like the SMSG materials, they have a conversational tone. Explanations and exercises are treated in an essentially conventional way, but there are many comments and questions which encourage independent thinking and action. Unit 6, on symmetry, has an instance where the child is told that the artist did not forget to put in the next design: "He said that it's your turn to make a design of your very own." [11]

In contrast to the other five programs is the Madison Project, in which methodology is integral to the content. Informal conversations and carefully sequenced questioning lead children to learn "from the intrinsic structure of the subject itself." [12] Active participation in discovering ideas in mathematics is basic to the program. Extensive aid to teachers is available from the project through which teachers learn to use methods of inquiry instead of imparting facts. Examples of questions employed in the Madison approach are:

> Does that seem to work?
>
> Do you have any other suggestions?
>
> Was that too big or too small?
>
> Shall we try that out?
>
> How can we do this?

A major value of the Madison Project lies in its adaptability for use as a supplement to any regular K–9 curriculum. This supplement would stress algebraic ideas and their symbolic representation.

Perhaps the only prominent methodological approach common to all six projects is that of emphasis on structure or pattern. This structural aspect of mathematics, which involves the ability to abstract and generalize, is concisely characterized by Van Engen:

> Structure as a mathematician uses this word . . . can be described as a search for patterns; patterns which can be used to arrive at solutions to problems. . . .
>
> . . . . .
>
> This approach solves whole classes or groups of problems simultaneously. It is a powerful method which rests on abstractions and generalizations of a high order. [13]

In summary, the explicit commonalities of method of the six new mathematics programs studied may be stated as:

1. Emphasis on the structure of mathematics
2. Emphasis on the ability to generalize
3. Emphasis on thinking and reasoning
4. Emphasis on the ideas themselves rather than on mechanics, memorization, and drill

Methodological aims specifically stated in one or a few programs, and perhaps implicit in all six, include the following:

1. Helping children to view numeration as recording of information —to see mathematics as a language
2. Helping children to consider a range of alternatives in problem-solving
3. Helping children to participate actively, to learn through discovery
4. Helping teachers to use questioning as a means of instruction

SIGNIFICANCE OF THE COMMON ELEMENTS

The common content elements referred to in the preceding section have been incorporated into elementary mathematics curriculum because mathematicians have defined them as fundamental or unifying ideas in their field; the commonalities of method identified here have been deemed highly valuable in the teaching-learning process by educational specialists.

In Part II, the content elements are discussed in detail, aspects of their historical development are traced, and relationships to commonalities of method are indicated. The major portions of the material devoted to each element are based on the works of distinguished mathematics historians and scholars. Educational implications are considered at the end of each chapter.

"There is a living, dynamic, propelling quality in man's creations, revealed through history," states Frances Minor; historical search can help children to establish an identification with the mainstream of mankind and, more particularly, an "identification of self with time past as one seeks rootedness in time present." [14] Understanding of the growth of key mathematical ideas through the ages will enable students to grasp more fully the significance of mathematics in their own lives and times.

Part II

KEY ELEMENTS

Their Origins and Evolution

The schoolboy's charge of dryness must be met by showing him how the progress of the arithmetic, geometry, algebra, and trigonometry that he is learning has gone on in answer to the needs that men have felt, and the desires they have formed.   —G. HEPPEL [1]

Thus, in 1893, reasoned an English mathematician, in a strong plea for providing historical context for the study of mathematics.

Heppel's major thesis was that the learner is aided by an awareness of historical order and by an understanding of the relationships among the aims of practical men, the progress of theory, and methods of computation. He cited ways in which mathematical discoveries have served commerce and navigation. These discoveries stemmed first from practical man's needs or wants, and through this channel led to key contributions of a few mathematical theorists. Ultimately a significant advance in theoretical knowledge provided benefit and learning for many.

A case, perhaps still debatable, for an even more imperative emphasis on knowledge of the past is cited by Herbert Spencer:

> The education of the child must accord both in mode and arrangement with the education of mankind as considered historically; or in other words, the genesis of knowledge in the individual must follow the same course as the genesis of knowledge in the race. To M. Comte we believe society owes the enunciation of this doctrine. . . .[2]

Among contemporary mathematicians, Morris Kline employs a historical approach. In the preface of his *Mathematics in Western Culture*

31

(1953), Kline speaks of the historical method as the "natural way of examining how the ideas arose, what the motivations for investigating these ideas were, and how these ideas influenced the course of other activities."

Some of the most fundamental mathematical concepts had their origins in the everyday experiences of prehistoric man. Knowledge of such experiential beginnings can lend depth to our comprehension of the functions of the concepts themselves.

The chapters to follow describe highlights in the historical development of key aspects of six areas of mathematics. The areas are treated in the order of their chronological emergence, although some overlap in time as well as substance is inevitable: (1) numeration systems; (2) measurement; (3) geometric ideas; (4) algebraic ideas; (5) structure (laws and systems); (6) sets.

Man's various roles—as discoverer, deviser, inventor, adapter, delineator, analyst, user—in the genesis and progressive development of concepts, symbols, and applications are depicted, and relationships between certain basic human needs and traits and the growth of certain mathematical ideas are traced. The material is offered as a broadly meaningful context for important content in mathematics education.

FOUR

Numeration

IDEAS ABOUT COUNTING

A numeration system may be defined as a method of recording quantitative information. The system of numeration in current use in most of the world is referred to as a decimal system. It is so designated because its units are in multiples of ten, each unit being ten times the unit next smaller.

The word *decimal* derives from the Latin *decem* ("ten"), which is found in words like *December,* the tenth month of the year of the ancient Roman calendar, and *decimate,* which referred to the punishment by death of each tenth soldier who had taken part in a mutiny. The word *dime* comes from the same root word.

The advantages of studying various systems of numeration, especially the nondecimal ones, have been cited frequently in the current literature. The 1963 Yearbook of NCTM mentions the following advantages:

1. Teachers may realize for the first time that it is possible for a place value system to use one of several grouping plans.

2. Teachers may experience, through working with non-decimal systems, a struggle similar to that which children encounter in working with the decimal plan. As a result, these teachers gain a better understanding of the problems of learning place value notation, and consequently they have more patience with children.

3. Children extend their knowledge of the principle of place value to the reading and writing of numerals in other bases.

4. Children develop additional insight into the fundamental operations of addition, multiplication, subtraction, and division, through performing these operations in a non-decimal numeration system.[1]

The authors of *Extending Mathematics Understanding* refer to four concepts to be developed in the study of numeration systems:

    1. Systems of numeration are man-made.
    2. Our numeral system has developed over a long period of time.
    3. Some understanding of other systems of numeration will enhance our understanding of our own system.
    4. Children can be led to appreciate the utility of the modern decimal system by learning about other systems.[2]

The ten numerical symbols in current use (0, 1, 2, 3, 4, 5, 6, 7, 8, 9) are usually taken for granted; they serve so efficiently that most people do not stop to wonder how and why they have acquired their present form and meaning. Yet each has its own individual history.

"As to the structure of the number language," writes Dantzig, "philological researches disclose an almost universal uniformity. Everywhere the ten fingers of man have left their permanent imprint."[3] The very early use of numbers was so closely tied to a display of fingers that there was an actual identity of these meanings; this led to calling the first ten numerals "digits"; the word itself is derived from the Latin *digitus*, meaning "finger."

There is evidence that in the beginning man first used his fingers and then other devices, such as pebbles in sand, notches in wood, knots in a rope, to record the passing of days or how many of something he had. This concept of one-to-one correspondence, a fundamental principle in mathematics, unquestionably had its origin in the early days of human existence. As long as the quantity to be recorded was relatively limited, the procedure of one-to-one correspondence met the need of people to keep track of things. When the need was for recording larger quantities, *tallying* was found to be convenient, as it still is today to keep score in a game. One has only to place his thumb across his palm in order to see the physiognomic paradigm for tallying four vertical strokes and covering them with a diagonal, thus representing a group of five.

And so it may be said that the development of the decimal system was based on a physiological accident. Indeed, as Florian Cajori has pointed out, there is a physiognomic basis for most of man's systems of numeration:

> Nearly all number systems, both ancient and modern, are based on the scale of 5, 10, or 20. The reason for this it is not difficult to see. When a child learns to count, he makes use of his fingers and perhaps of his toes. In the same way the savages of prehistoric times unquestionably counted on their fingers and in some cases also on their toes.[4]

Deriving names and symbols to represent particular quantities was among man's first numeration problems. In *Numbers and Numerals*, Smith and Ginsburg say that number names were among the first words people used when they began to talk. These writers refer to the savage's grunt *"ung"* (so like the present French *un*), which meant "one," and also illustrate the likeness of number names in several different languages. Part of their listing is shown here: [5]

Modern English	French	German	Old English	Latin	Greek
one	un	ein	an	unus	oinos
two	deux	zwei	two	duo	duo
three	trois	drei	threo	tres	treis

Smith and Ginsburg also point out that in many languages the words meaning "first" and "second" are not derived from the words meaning "one" and "two," which suggests that in early times people did not connect the idea of "one" with "first" and that of "two" with "second"; the *cardinal–ordinal* relationship was not recognized until quite some time later in the development of the human race.[6] (The cardinal numbers—1, 2, 3, . . .—answer the question *how many?* The ordinal numbers—1st, 2nd, 3rd, . . .—answer the question *which one,* or *where in the order?*) It was from the principle of one-to-one correspondence, used in counting, that the concept of cardinal numbers was eventually derived, the word *cardinal* having been chosen from the Latin *cardo,* meaning pivot, hinge, or turning point. Smith characterizes a cardinal number as one on which arithmetic turns, or depends.[7]

It is interesting to note, too, the origin of number names for quantities over ten. The word "eleven" comes from an old Teutonic word *ainlif,* meaning "one left over" (after counting ten); *twalif* ("twelve") meant "two left over"; "thirteen" is a slurring of "three and ten," and "twenty" is a corruption of "twain (two) tens."

With names for numbers established, the need for symbolic representation for these quantitative ideas followed:

> We do not know how long ago it was that human beings first began to make their thoughts known to one another by means of speech; but it seems probable that people learned to use words in talking many thousands of years before they learned to set down these words in writing. In the same way, after people learned to name numbers it took a long time for them to learn to use signs for the numbers; for example, to use the numeral "2" instead of the word "two." [8]

It is probable that the first few Hindu-Arabic numeration symbols, like the base of the decimal system, had their origin in the human hand.

Parallel horizontal or vertical strokes, used by the ancients to represent "one," "two," and "three," readily suggest the fingers of the hand:

Moreover, Smith and Ginsburg have pointed out that when we write two or three such lines very quickly, so that they become connected, the forms of the modern symbols 2 and 3 begin to emerge.[9] That the Roman V can be seen as the shape of a hand probably accounts for this symbol representing the value of five. Two hands, one upside down, $\overset{\vee}{\wedge}$, suggest the Roman X, the symbol for ten.

This capacity for symbolic representation was crucial not only to mathematics annotation but also to the entire development of language and written communication. The authors of *The Number Story* emphasize a consequent aspect of mathematical progress:

> Even after our prehistoric ancestor had already established some names for counting, he would have thought "three bears," or "three trees" but not of "three." The step from understanding threesomes of that kind to understanding "three" is an enormous advance, and marks the initial important climb in mathematics.[10]

ANCIENT SYSTEMS

An examination of how various cultures have dealt with problems of recording numerical data shows that man has coped with the quantitative situations in his environment in different ways, at different stages in time.

Although the hypothetical average citizen probably tends to take numbers even as large as one thousand for granted, the person who is prone to reflection has no doubt recognized that a great deal of complex information is encoded in even a small and simple number. It may appear superfluous to state that 1752 means one thousand plus seven hundreds plus five tens plus two ones. The fact is that many hundreds of years of evolution have gone into this numerical notation system and highly significant mathematical concepts are involved. These concepts may appear quite self-evident, but the fact that they were neither available nor evident to highly skilled mathematicians in ancient times is proof of their profundity.

The principle of *place value* or *positional value*, for example, refers to the fact that the spatial relationship of one symbol to another determines a large measure of that symbol's quantitative value. It is easy, today, to recognize that 12 means something very different from 21, even though the same symbols are employed.

Table 3 illustrates a number of ancient numeration systems and the characteristics and principles of their use. It can be seen that the principle of place value as later developed was missed by these ancient systems; and there are other analogues to the modern system of today. A study of this summary of eight ancient systems of numeration, spanning a period of about five thousand years, will make evident the evolutionary nature of the modern system.

The *additive principle* governs cases in which the value represented by each individual symbol is added to that of another one—usually the symbol immediately preceding—in representing a given number. Primitive examples are tallies: ||| for three (one plus one plus one); ||||| || for seven (five ones plus two ones). The ancient Roman notation of VIII, for five plus three (one five plus three ones), is easily recognized even today because of its continued use for all these hundreds of years. The Babylonian ⟨⟨ ҮҮҮ stood for twenty-six (two tens plus six ones). In the modern decimal system the additive principle also operates: 26 means 2 tens plus 6 ones.

The *subtractive principle* applies when it is understood that a smaller quantity is to be taken away from a larger one in order to express a particular value. In the Roman system (where the principle was a late development and involved positional significance), the symbol IV indicated that one was to be subtracted from five to represent four; the symbol XL meant L minus X, or fifty minus ten. The Babylonian symbol for subtraction was Ү⟩ ; the number 28 was written as ⟨⟨⟨ Ү ҮҮ , indicating thirty minus two.

The *multiplicative principle* is employed when all or part of a numeral is to be multiplied by a particular quantity, such as 10, 100, or 1000. This is shown by a special symbol. In the Roman system, a bar over a number indicated multiplication by one thousand; thus $\overline{XII}$ stood for 12,000.

The symbols employed in the eight systems may be categorized as follows: (1) letters of the alphabet, (2) arbitrary symbols (dashes, strokes, etc.), and (3) picture writing figures which resemble familiar objects or suggest ideas associated with the objects. Mueller emphasizes the importance of differentiating between the fundamental principles of a system and the symbols through which these principles are manifest. The choice of symbols is essentially arbitrary and bears little actual relationship to the system itself; it is the principles of a system that give it structure and organization, thereby influencing the application of the symbols to mathematical problems.[11]

Systems based on human anatomy are those structured according to multiples of 5, 10, or 20. Of these, 10 is the most common base. Only

TABLE 3 : SYSTEMS OF NUMERATION OVER FIVE

System	Symbols											Principles
Early Egyptian (c. 3500 B.C.)	1 vertical stroke	10 heel bone	100 scroll	1000 lotus flower	10,000 pointed finger	100,000 burbot (fish)	1,000,000 man in astonishment					• Addition • Repetition
Chinese-Japanese (One of the oldest systems; date uncertain; developed by the Chinese; later adopted by the Japanese)	1	2	3	4	5	6	7	8	9	10	100 1000	• Addition • Multiplication
Mayan (Remote origin; date uncertain; assigned to 200-600 A.D. by some historians)	1	2	3	4	5	6	7	8	9	10	19 0	• Addition • Multiplication • Repetition • Positional grouping for numbers over 20
Babylonian (c. 2000 B.C. - 200 B.C.)	1	10	100		Symbol for subtraction: Symbol for zero: (c. 200 B.C.)							• Addition • Subtraction • Multiplication • Repetition • Positional grouping for numbers over 60
Greek (Attic or Herodianic) System (c. 300 B.C.; used as early as 600 B.C.)	1 Iota	5 Pente	10 Deka	100 Hekaton	1000 Chilioi	10,000 Myrioi						• Addition • Multiplication • Repetition
Greek (Alexandrian) System (c. 400 B.C.; used concurrently with above)	1 A′ 10 I′ 100 P′	2 B′ 20 K′ 200 Σ′	3 Γ′ 30 Λ′ 300 T′	4 Δ′ 40 M′ 400 γ′	5 E′ 50 N′ 500 Φ′	6 F′ 60 Ξ′ 600 X′	7 Z′ 70 O′ 700 Ψ′	8 H′ 80 II′ 800 Ω′	9 θ′ 90 Q′ 900 Z′			• Addition • Multiplication for numbers over 10,000
Roman (c. 500 B.C. c. 1600 A.D.)	1 I	5 V	10 X	50 L	100 C	500 D	1000 M					• Addition • Repetition • Subtraction • Multiplication for numbers over 1000
Hindu-Arabic (without zero, c. 200 A.D.; with zero, c. 500 A.D. - present; came into full use in the sixteenth century)	0	1	2	3	4	5	6	7	8	9		• Addition • Positional value

THOUSAND YEARS: SOME BASIC CHARACTERISTICS

Base	Examples	Other Characteristics and Comments
10	5 ⁞⁞⁞ ⁞⁞ 42 ∩∩∩∩ ⁞⁞ 2,317 𓏤 𓏤 𝟡𝟡𝟡 ∩ ⁞⁞⁞	• Symbols for larger values written first. • A later system of Egyptian hieroglyphics was a ciphered one; the differences are much the same as those between the two Greek systems illustrated below.
10	826 八 百 From top down: 二 8 × 100 十 2 × 10 六 and 6	• Interesting resemblance to the Hindu-Arabic system which can be seen more clearly when the Hindu-Arabic number is written in expanded form: 826 = 8(100) + 2(10) + 6
20	200 (ten twenties) 340 (17 twenties) 360 (1 × 20 × 18)	• Use of zero (in the form of an oval) which was not common to other systems. • Positional principle; numbers written vertically with lowest value at the bottom. • Adding one oval below a number made it 20 times larger; adding a second oval multiplied the number by 18. The moon calendar of 360 days probably accounted for this plan.
10 and 60	46 ‹‹‹‹ 𝍫 17 ‹‹ Υ 𝍫 (20−3) 300,972 Υ ‹‹ ΥΥΥ ‹‹‹ 𝍫 ‹ΥΥ 1(60³) + 23(60²) + 38(60¹) + 12	• Wedge-shaped symbols called cuneiform — probably developed by early Sumerians. • First trace of subtraction found in this system of notation. • Inclusion of a symbol for zero to denote absence of a figure (c. 200 B.C.); not used for computation. • Sexagesimal (base 60) system used chiefly for weights and measurement; an example of place value in rudimentary form.
10	4,878 ΧΧΧΧ Γᴴ ΗΗΗ Γᴬ ΔΔ Υ⁞⁞⁞ (4000) + (500) + (300) + (50) + (28)	• Six symbol system with each symbol named for the initial alphabet letter of its name; symbol for 5 combined with other symbols to indicate larger numbers.
10	28 ΚΉ΄ 354 ΤΝΔ΄ 1,000 ͵Α (multiples of 1,000 were shown by an accent sign to the left of the letter) 20,000 Μ (multiples of 10,000 were represented by M combined with other symbols)	• Ciphered system using the existing 24 letter alphabet plus three other symbols. • More compact than earlier system; harder on memory; an example of the fact that science does not always move in a forward direction. • An accent sign or bar was used to denote numerical value rather than letter value. • Less conducive to computation than earlier system, Egyptian system or Roman system.
10	3 III 100,000 C̄ 12 XII 14 XIV 3,000 I̅I̅I̅	• Symbols are mostly unused relics of the Greek alphabet representing powers of ten. • The subtractive principle was adopted at a later time for more economical notation; it is used only with fours and nines. This is an early instance of the order principle which became basic to the present system.
10		• A complete system requiring no new symbols regardless of how large a number is to be expressed. Basic structure provides for great ease in computation.

in recent centuries has it been discovered that systems based on 5 and 20 were used by cultures previously unknown. Cajori points out that lower cultures tended to use a base of 5 or 20, while cultures achieving a higher degree of civilization tended toward a base of 10, finding 5 too limited and 20 too cumbersome.[12]

The Babylonian, Egyptian, Chinese–Japanese, Greek, and Roman notations all employed a base of 10, using the additive principle by itself or combined with the subtractive or multiplicative principle. Only in the Babylonian sexagesimal system and in the old Chinese–Japanese system is the concept of place value evident. (The best historical evidence indicates that different cultures discovered this principle independently.) And in the Babylonian system there is a record of a symbol for zero (c. 200 B.C.) consisting of two marks $\lessgtr$ which were used to indicate the absence of a numeral, but not for purposes of computation.[13] These are rudimentary instances of the two ideas which were eventually to revolutionize mathematical notation.

The full development of our decimal notation, as Cajori indicates, belongs to comparatively modern times:

> Decimal notation had been in use for thousands of years, before it was perceived that its simplicity and usefulness could be enormously increased by the adoption of the principle of position. To the Hindus of the fifth and sixth century after Christ we owe the full systematic development of the use of zero and the principle of local value. Of all the mathematical discoveries, no one has contributed more to the general progress of intelligence than this. While the older notations served merely to record the answer of an arithmetical computation, the Hindu notation (wrongly called the Arabic notation) assists with marvellous power in performing the computation itself.[14]

Little is known regarding the development of Hindu notation, but it is thought to have originated in Ceylon, to have had only nine symbols (no zero) at about A.D. 200, and to have reached Europe in its developed form during the twelfth century:

> The Hindu notation . . . was transmitted to the Occident through the Arabs, hence the name "Arabic notation." No blame attaches to the Arabs for this pseudo-name; they always acknowledged the notation as an inheritance from India. During the 1000 years preceding 1200 A.D., the Hindu numerals and notation, while in the various stages of evolution, were carried from country to country. Exactly what these migrations were, is a problem of extreme difficulty.[15]

Historians differ in their explanations regarding the origin and transmission of Hindu notation. That there has been considerable

change in the form of the symbols over the centuries, however, has
been generally acknowledged. Illustrations of such change are provided in Table 4. These are included in order to counteract the notion,
too frequently encountered, that contemporary notational symbols have
always been as they are today, and to show how they gradually developed out of accumulated knowledge and experience of the past.
For example, as already noted, the present symbols 2 and 3 probably
grew out of ancient man's commercial need to write $=$ and $\equiv$ very
quickly.

The wide differences in the recorded forms of numerical symbols in
past centuries are probably due to the fact that they were hand-
written. The forms did not become stabilized until the invention of
printing. So strong an influence was the advent of printing that the
appearance of present-day numerals and those of the fifteenth century
are essentially the same, as compared with the marked changes of
previous eras.[16] However, considering the great variety of printing type

Table 4

Early Forms of Hindu-Arabic Numerals

Year	1	2	3	4	5	6	7	8	9	0
976 A.D.[a]	1	ζ	ξ	γ	Y	b	7	8	9	
1360 A.D.[b]	1	ζ	3	又	4	6	Λ	8	9	0
1453 A.D.[c]	1	2	3	又	4	6	Λ	8	9	0

[a] From the oldest definitely dated European manuscript, *Codex Vigilanus*,
written in Spain in the year A.D. 976. Taken from G. F. Hill, *The Development of Arabic Numerals in Europe* (London: Oxford University Press,
1915), Table I, pp. 28-29.

[b] From a manuscript in the British Museum. Taken from David Eugene
Smith and Louis Charles Karpinski, *The Hindu-Arabic Numerals* (Boston:
Ginn and Company, 1911), p. 143. Hill, on p. 31 of his book (1915), questions the date: "Smith and Karpinski say that this MS. contains the date
1360, to which year (apparently in error) they accordingly assign it." Hill
dates the sample earlier—as 13th century after 1264.

[c] As shown on a portable brass sundial of German origin, in the British
Museum. Taken from Hill (1915), Table XXXVI, pp. 84-85. In the same
table are almost identical numerals appearing on a 1491 Viennese astrolabe,
also in the British Museum.

faces available today, there is no guarantee that these symbols will not change their forms in the future.

Zero was the last of the ten symbols to be introduced into the present system. The word is derived from the Hindu *sunya*, meaning empty or vacant. In the tenth century the Arabs adopted the Indian system and translated *sunya* according to their word *sifr*, meaning empty space. The word *sifr* has undergone many changes—the Italians expressed it as *zephirum*, the Germans as *cifra;* in English *cifra* became *cipher*, which means absence of quantity, the original meaning of zero.[17]

At first, zero was used only as a place holder, a symbol for nothing; it was not recognized as a number which could be operated upon like other numbers.[18] (For example, zero can be added to another number: $7+0=7$. In contrast, "7+ nothing" has no meaning.) Of its immense importance as a place-holder, Dantzig says:

> Conceived in all probability as the symbol for an empty column on a counting board [abacus °], the Indian *sunya* was destined to become the turning point in a development without which the progress of modern science, industry, or commerce is inconceivable. And the influence of this great discovery was by no means confined to arithmetic. By paving the way to a generalized number concept, it played just as fundamental a role in practically every branch of mathematics. In the history of culture the discovery of zero will always stand out as one of the greatest single achievements of the human race.[19]

Many ancient cultures attained a relatively high degree of civilization and contributed a rich heritage in fields such as literature, art, music, and philosophy. But the failure of the ancients to recognize the value of a symbol for the empty column as well as a need for a positional principle thwarted mathematical progress for almost five thousand years.

Dantzig points out that this principle is actually inherent in our number language and that "the first attempt to translate the action of the counting board into the language of numerals ought to have resulted in the discovery of the principle of position." [20] The principle of place value is, after all, usually learned easily by the average school child of today.

The fact that such a simple and fundamental observation was overlooked even by the most gifted of ancient mathematicians has remained a source of wonder to this day. However, it is no doubt true that com-

---

° The abacus is a mechanical device used in computation, on which a disc or pebble-like object represents a unit. The abacus came into use to meet commercial needs in ancient times and is still used in various circumstances (as for teaching the meaning of place value in arithmetic).

parable undiscovered relationships exist today, and that future generations will wonder at the apparent blindness of the sages of the present
era.

MODERN NONDECIMAL SYSTEMS

The ten fingers of man have been the primary influence in the evolution of a base-ten system of numeration. The two fundamental principles on which this decimal system is based are (1) place value in
which a symbol has both an absolute and a positional value, and (2) the
use of zero, a symbol to indicate *not any*.

In the study of modern nondecimal systems it is helpful to note two
other descriptive characteristics of the base-ten system: (1) There are
as many distinct symbols as the name of the base; that is, there are ten
symbols. (2) The highest symbol, in terms of absolute value, is one less
than the name of the base; that is, the highest symbol is 9.

Had man been born with either fewer or more fingers than ten, it is
highly probable that civilization today would be recording quantitative
information in multiples of whatever number of fingers human beings
possessed. A modern nondecimal system based on multiples of any
number (except one) would have the same characteristics regarding
symbols as mentioned above; that is, it would have as many symbols as
the name, with the highest symbol being one less than the name. For
example, a base-four system would have four symbols (0, 1, 2, 3), the
highest being 3. A base-twelve system would require twelve symbols,
including two new ones (not present in the decimal system) to represent ten and eleven. Most textbooks today use t and e for this purpose.
Thus, the symbols for a base-twelve system would look like this: 0, 1,
2, 3, 4, 5, 6, 7, 8, 9, t, e. Then the symbol 10 would represent one twelve
and no ones. To clarify these characteristic similarities of nondecimal
numeration systems, some counting numbers in several different base
systems are shown in Table 5.

The following place value chart is a structural representation of the
decimal system:

. . .	1000's	100's	10's	1's	10ths	. . .

A more scientific way of representing this structure is:

. . .	10^3	10^2	10^1	10^0	10^{-1}	. . .

Table 5

Notation for Some Counting Numbers in Six Different Base Systems

Base 12	Base 10	Base 8	Base 5	Base 4	Base 2
1	**1**	1	1	1	1
2	**2**	2	2	2	**10**
3	**3**	3	3	3	11
4	**4**	4	4	**10**	100
5	**5**	5	**10**	11	101
6	**6**	6	11	12	110
7	**7**	7	12	13	111
8	**8**	**10**	13	20	1000
9	**9**	11	14	21	1001
t	**10**	12	20	22	1010
e	**11**	13	21	23	1011
10	**12**	14	22	30	1100
. . .	. . .	. . .	. . .	. . .	. . .
13	**15**	17	30	33	1111
. . .	. . .	. . .	. . .	. . .	. . .
18	**20**	24	40	110	10100
19	**21**	25	41	111	10101
1t	**22**	26	42	112	10110
1e	**23**	27	43	113	10111
20	**24**	30	44	120	11000
21	**25**	31	100	121	11001

NOTE: In each base, the symbol **10** represents the base number or name. In base ten, **10** means *one ten* and no ones; in base four, **10** means *one four* and no ones; in base twelve, **10** means *one twelve* and no ones; and so forth.

The exponents (small raised numerals) indicate the number of times the base ten is used as a factor in the different columns. For example, $10^2 = 10 \times 10$ (ten is used twice as a factor), and $10^3 = 10 \times 10 \times 10$. Any quantity "to the zero power" (with a zero exponent) is always equal to *one;* it is so defined by mathematicians because this is internally consistent with mathematical structure. Accordingly, a negative exponent represents a fractional part of the base to which it refers.

Using a place value chart, any decimal system number may be represented by entering its digits in the appropriate columns. For example, the numbers 28, 354, and 4,985.3 would be represented as follows:

	10^3 (1000's)	10^2 (100's)	10^1 (10's)	10^0 (1's)	10^{-1} (10ths)	
. . .			2	8		. . . .
		3	5	4		
	4	9	8	5	3	

These numbers can also be written in these expanded forms:

$$28 = 2(10) + 8(1) \quad \text{or} \quad 2(10^1) + 8(10^0)$$
$$354 = 3(100) + 5(10) + 4(1) \quad \text{or} \quad 3(10^2) + 5(10^1) + 4(10^0)$$
$$4985.3 = 4(1000) + 9(100) + 8(10) + 5(1) + 3(.1)$$
$$\text{or} \quad 4(10^3) + 9(10^2) + 8(10^1) + 5(10^0) + 3(10^{-1})$$

Both the place value chart and the expanded notations highlight the structural aspects of the decimal system. Decimal system numerals are simply coefficients of understood powers of base ten, the power being specifically determined by the position of the numeral. (A coefficient is any symbol, such as a numeral or letter, placed before another symbol or combination of symbols as a multiplier.) In 354, for example, 3 is the coefficient of 10^2, 5 is the coefficient of 10^1, and 4 is the coefficient of 10^0.

The superiority of the place value notation can be readily appreciated when one considers how cumbersome it would be to keep records with numbers written in expanded form. (The Chinese-Japanese system sketched in Table 3 used an expanded notation.)

Expressing a given quantity in several different base systems of numeration serves to delineate a common structural component and to highlight significant relationships. The material below shows how 35_{10} is written in number systems of bases four, five, twelve, and two. (The subscript numeral designates the base in which a number is expressed; 35_{10} is read "thirty-five base ten.")

Base 10: 35_{10}

10^2	10^1	10^0
	3	5

$$3(10^1) + 5(10^0) =$$
$$30 + 5 = 35$$

Base 4: 203_4

4^2	4^1	4^0
2	0	3

$$2(4^2) + 0(4^1) + 3(4^0) =$$
$$32 + 0 + 3 = 35$$

Base 5: 120_5

5^2	5^1	5^0
1	2	0

$$1(5^2) + 2(5^1) + 0(5^0) =$$
$$25 + 10 + 0 = 35$$

Base 12: $2E_{12}$

12^2	12^1	12^0
	2	E

$$2(12^1) + E(12^0) =$$
$$2(12) + 11(1) =$$
$$24 + 11 = 35$$

Base 2: 100011_2

2^5	2^4	2^3	2^2	2^1	0^0
1	0	0	0	1	1

$$1(2^5) + 0(2^4) + 0(2^3) + 0(2^2) + 1(2^1) + 1(2^0) =$$
$$1(32) + 0(16) + 0(8) + 0(4) + 1(2) + 1(1) =$$
$$32 + 0 + 0 + 0 + 2 + 1 = 35$$

Summarized: $35_{10} = 203_4 = 120_5 = 2E_{12} = 100011_2$.

The notational change when a value expressed in one numeration system is then expressed in another system represents a redistribution of this quantity according to multiples of a new unit. A simple way, then, to express a base-ten value in another base system is to (1) make a place value chart for the new base, and (2) distribute the given base-ten quantity according to the multiples of the new unit. (To begin, it is necessary to determine what the largest power of the new base will be, by quickly finding the largest one that is *contained* in the value of the base ten number. For example, in base 4 the powers are $4^0 = 1$, $4^1 = 4$, $4^2 = 16$, $4^3 = 64$, ... To express 35_{10} in base 4, then, note that 35 is between 16 and 64. How many 64's are contained in 35? Answer: none. So the new number will start with a multiple of 4^2. How many 16's are contained in 35? Answer: *two*, with 3 ones left over to distribute. How many 4's are contained in 3? Answer: *none*. How many 1's are contained in 3? Answer: *three*.)

And note that writing a number in a base other than ten in its expanded form and doing the indicated operations, yields its base-ten equivalent.

In all the place value charts shown above for specific base systems, a pattern emerges which can be generalized and illustrated as follows with b standing for any base:

. . .	b^4	b^3	b^2	b^1	b^0	b^{-1}	b^{-2}	. . .

This is a key aspect of modern numeration systems, a part of fundamental structure—a concept which when understood frees one to work productively with such systems and others that are similar.

IMPLICATIONS FOR EDUCATION

When students have an opportunity to study various systems of numeration—ancient and modern—they are thereby given a view in depth of many of the most profound aspects of culture and civilization. The ancient Greeks believed that mathematics was the purest of the sciences and were particularly averse to what would presently be called the applied sciences. They felt that mathematics contained the distilled essence of logical thought unencumbered by earthly irrelevancies. Today it is often thought that the pendulum has swung to the opposite extreme and that science is more valued for its practical applications than for basic theory. Nevertheless, mathematics is the one science which has come closest to remaining "pure." One may become a first-rate mathematical theorist without being in the least concerned with concrete objects or events in the world of reality.

It was in the late 1600's that Leibniz developed the binary system of numeration, a base-two system which has only two symbols, 0 and 1. But it wasn't until the introduction of electronic computers in the 1940's that the binary system came into practical use. Electrical circuits with an *on* position for 1 and an *off* position for 0 need no more than two symbols to accomplish computation of unusual complexity in a few minutes. Computers today employ several different base systems depending upon the nature of the problem "fed" into them.

In studying systems of numeration the student is exposed not only to methods of annotating quantitative data but also to problems of performing with these data and keeping records of the operations involved. Teachers who are aware of these implications have the opportunity of introducing their students to an entire range of complex processes which are at the very heart of the progress of civilization.*

Although to a certain extent a similar claim may be made for other topics, both in mathematics and other fields of knowledge, systems of numeration present a challenging opportunity for thought which is almost unique. Most children come to school able to count to ten or beyond. Since this learning has already taken place in the preschool years, the child "naturally" feels that his method of counting is the only available means of dealing with quantitative problems. This childhood belief is reinforced by the fact that many parents have similar beliefs and by the fact that all of the child's friends and acquaintances use the same numbers, based on multiples of ten, for counting. If the child happens to know—or later to learn—another language, he will receive further reinforcement in the fact that this language also employs methods of enumeration and computation which are tied to the base of ten.

When the student is invited to consider that the very same data which have been counted by ten numerals can also be counted by eight or twelve or even two numerals, he comes face to face with the concept of relativity of means: The very same event may be effectively

* See Leonard Simon and Jeanne Bendick, *The Day the Numbers Disappeared* (1963), for introductory material prepared for children's use.

viewed or managed in various ways, depending upon the approach one wishes to take and the goals one has set.

It is likely that children are much less shaken by such a learning experience than their parents would be. With children the teacher has an opportunity to make the concept of the relativity of means an early and natural learning experience. With many of today's children already exposed to this kind of learning process, it is difficult even to imagine the effects of this generation's contribution to the rapid expansion of knowledge.

Beyond these influences upon ways of thinking and conceptualizing, there is also an opportunity for the appreciation of many facets of the history of civilizations. The student may be introduced to the needs of primitive man for counting his herds, to the beliefs of ancient Babylonians in connection with astronomical computations, and to the vast business and commercial intricacies of the Roman empire.

Through this way of learning the student gains a feeling for the historical process. His knowledge becomes deepened and less fragmented, as he gains a firm grasp of important ideas and how they came about and how they fit into a still larger complex of ideas. This understanding of the history of people and of ideas should give the student a fuller comprehension of the vast events in the world around him. The appreciation of concepts and events and movements of civilization may serve to free students to be creative in their own right. If the student recognizes that a given problem can be conceptualized in different and equally valid modes, he may well be encouraged to develop his individual mode and eventually make a significant contribution of his own. The importance of these aspects of mathematics learning cannot be overstated.

The many technological challenges of the space age also present myriad opportunities for scientific discovery. Enormous scientific advances which have taken place in the past decade could never have evolved without the tools that mathematics has made available.

The need for ultra-precise and incredibly rapid computation has been highlighted by the onboard computers of the space rockets. The increasing complexity of mankind's problems in all areas of living will necessitate commensurate precision and capacity for huge loads of data in a number of different directions.

In many ways the age of computers seems on the verge of arriving—a fact which is bound to influence almost every facet of civilization. The development of new machines and the programing of material for them can only be accomplished by human beings. It is self-evident that the school curriculum must prepare many of today's young people for this future role.

FIVE

Measurement

IDEAS ABOUT UNITS

Nearly every aspect of contemporary civilization depends on the concept of measurement and on its application, ranging from the relatively simple measurements needed for the manufacture of clothing to the highly complex measurements required to send a spacecraft into orbit. The construction of every home, as well as its plumbing, heating, air-conditioning, and other conveniences, is wholly dependent upon measurement for ultimate efficient functioning.

Although arithmetic as a science does not depend on measurement, a very large proportion of both adult and child *applications* of arithmetic is related to measurement.[1] Transportation and mass communication media could not have developed to their present state without the use of highly precise measurement techniques. In any musical score, in the work of any graphic artist, the idea of measurement is inherent; many sports, games, and other leisure activities require means of measurement. In international commerce, a system of established and standardized measures is absolutely vital to such matters as monetary exchange and freighting of cargo. In its most exacting form, measurement is fundamental to medical science and to every scientific advance man has achieved or will achieve in the future.

The literature of the various social and physical sciences shows marked evidence of continuous concern with problems of measurement and evaluation. In December 1956, the American Association for the Advancement of Science held a symposium on measurement. The papers presented were concerned both with meanings and theories of measurement and with problems of measurement in the physical and social sciences. Many different viewpoints emerged, and the symposium as a whole contributed a general picture of the concerns of scientists in the foundations of measurement in the middle of the twentieth century. The editors of the collected papers note an interesting contrast between the concerns of the physicists and those of the behavioral scientists: "The physicists are concerned with problems of measurement arising from accepted models, whereas the behavioral scientists are concerned with problems of measurement arising from proposed empirical studies." [2] The details of the contributions made are not discussed here because they are considerably beyond the interest and ability of the elementary school child and are not necessary background for teachers at that level. The focus of the symposium is mentioned as evidence of the prominence of measurement in contemporary science.

Certain measurement concepts can be included in the elementary school curriculum as part of liberal education and as preparation for later work involving more complex measurement ideas and their implementation. In *Extending Mathematics Understanding* seven concepts considered central to this area of mathematics are identified:

1. The defined unit of measure is exact; any reproduction of such a unit is an approximation.
2. Measurements are applications of defined units of measure and [are] approximate.
3. Both direct and indirect measurements are made.
4. Our units of measure were chosen by man.
5. Units of measure are continually evolving.
6. The evolution of units of measure has been in the direction of standardized units.
7. There is appreciable difference in the size of units expressed by the same name in various countries of the world. [3]

It is not the purpose of this chapter to explain the various types of measurements, their units and application, but rather to discuss the nature of measurement and its unifying ideas. It is in such a context that the study of any particular type of measurement can be most meaningfully pursued by teachers and students.

UNITS AND INSTRUMENTS

The *Encyclopaedia Britannica* (1952) defines "measurement" in this way:

> The determination of the magnitude of anything in terms of a suitable unit. Such units may be quite arbitrary, e.g., the pound, foot, second or degree centigrade, or may be derived from a combination of the arbitrary units, e.g., pounds per cubic foot. The procedure adopted

depends entirely on the nature of the quantity to be measured and on the accuracy required.

More simply, measurement involves a comparison with a standard unit of measure, this unit having been arbitrarily determined.

The classic literature of the English language contains references to many long outworn measures. In the Bible it is written: "The length of the ark shall be 300 cubits" (Genesis 7). In Shakespeare's *Tempest:* "Full fathom five thy father lies" (act 1, scene 2) and "Now would I give a thousand furlongs of sea" (act 1, scene 1). In Lincoln's Gettysburg Address: "Fourscore and seven years ago." In Tennyson's "Charge of the Light Brigade:" "Half a league, half a league, half a league on-ward." The magnitudes of the measures referred to in these quotations are: cubit—18 inches; fathom—6 feet; furlong—220 yards, ⅛ mile, or 40 rods; league—3 miles; score—20.

In common language today, people refer to measurements in such terms as these: length, width, area, volume, weight, time, temperature, speed, and distance. Other physical properties which can be measured include: power, force, work, light intensity, sound intensity, energy-producing value of food, distance over which light can travel in one year, and a variety of electric and magnetic quantities. All physical measurements such as these are considered properties of the thing being measured. In other words, it is not a table that is measured, but its length, width, or height.

For each measurement noted above, a standardized unit has been established (usually by law) and in some cases a specific instrument designed for making the measurement. This can be illustrated, in part, as follows:

Measurement	*Unit(s)*	*Instrument(s)*
Length	inches, feet, yards, millimeters, centi-meters, decimeters, meters	ruler, yardstick, meterstick
Weight	pounds, ounces, grams	scales
Temperature	degrees	thermometers (centi-grade, Fahrenheit)

Measurements of power (mechanical and derived) are expressed in terms of watts, electric current in amperes, electric potential in volts, and electric resistance in ohms. A number of different instruments and formulas are used to determine these measurements, a listing of which does not seem indicated here.

KEY IDEAS

The notion of number can be thought of in relation to material substance with separate component parts which can be placed in one-to-one correspondence with the counting numbers. It can also be thought of in connection with continuous magnitude—the magnitude of something whose elements cannot be placed in one-to-one correspondence with counting numbers. The former instance (counting) is the simplest and *only exact form of measurement,* although people do not usually think of it in those terms. All other forms are approximate. In the latter instance some method must be devised by which the continuous magnitude can be treated as if separated into equal parts. An arbitrarily designated unit is selected for this purpose. The equal "parts" can then be placed in one-to-one correspondence with the counting numbers and a quantitative evaluation of the whole can be determined. This process of finding the number of times a standard unit is contained within a continuous magnitude is usually referred to as measurement. Almost all modern measurement is of this nature.[4]

Some measurements can be determined by direct comparison, such as finding the length of a table by counting the number of linear units in its length. Other measurements must be derived either through calculation involving the use of algebraic or geometric formulas or by measuring some other quantity.

> Instruments such as clocks, thermometers, speedometers, and spring scales are used to make measurements indirectly. Such devices convert the quantity being measured into forces which move gears, expand metals, and in some way produce numbers which are read directly on a scale. Such measurements are made possible by combined mathematical, scientific, and mechanical knowledge. Some quantities are measured indirectly by using mathematical formulas to translate known direct measurements into a number for the quantity. The area of a rectangular floor is found indirectly when the number of units in the length and the number of units in the width are substituted in the formula $A = lw$.[5]

In order to understand the nature of degrees of approximation in measurement, a working knowledge of the following terms representing key ideas of measurement is essential:

Standard unit refers to an arbitrarily selected magnitude to be regarded as a single thing, an undivided whole.

Precision refers to the exactness of measurement and computation. It is determined by the size of the unit used for the measurement; the smaller the unit, the greater is the preciseness of the measurement. For example, a ruler graduated in sixteenths of an inch will afford a more precise measurement than one graduated in eighths of an inch.

Error refers to the difference between the actual, true, or correct measurement and the recorded measurement, which is approximate.

Lagest possible error (tolerance) refers to one-half the smallest unit of measurement. For example, the use of a ruler graduated in fourths of an inch involves a possible error of plus or minus one-eighth of an inch.

Accuracy (relative error) refers to the ratio of the largest possible error to the measured value. If, for instance, measurements for two different objects made with the same yardstick, graduated in inches, are given as 20 inches and 30 inches, the precision of the two measurements is the same, and the greatest possible error in each case is plus or minus one-half inch. The accuracy, or relative error, however, is *not* the same. The ratio of one-half inch to twenty inches is larger than the ratio of one-half inch to thirty inches.

An important differentiation between "unit" and "standard" should be recognized: "A unit is a quantity, magnitude, or value used. A standard is the physical model of any unit. The ideal standard should be available or reproducible by scientists anywhere." [6]

Until 1960, the international standard for linear measurement was a metal bar housed in a vault at the International Bureau of Weights and Measurements in France. The magnitude of such an object, as Schaaf points out, is not independent of physical conditions:

> Thus a standard yard has a length of one yard when at some definite temperature and supported in a certain manner; if supported in a different manner, it might have to be at a different temperature in order to have a length of a yard. [7]

By international agreement, the linear standard was changed in 1960 to the wave length of the orange-red light emitted by krypton-86 atoms. Because this light has an unchanging wave length, and because of the great precision (small magnitude) of this standard, the new unit of measure provides far greater accuracy in measurement than was ever possible before—about two parts in one billion, or about one meter of error in the distance between the earth and the moon. [8] An optical interferometer is the instrument used to count the number of wave lengths of light in a given distance. This present standard of length is reproducible in any laboratory.

In characteristic fashion, however, scientists are now working toward achieving an even more precise standard. The laser beam, perhaps the meter of the future, is likely to provide accuracy of better than one part in a trillion. [9]

DEVELOPMENTAL ROOTS

The development of measurement was not unlike that of numeration systems. In many ways their growth has been parallel. As speech developed among human beings with the need to communicate in matters of everyday life, so was there an early need to talk about things in terms of their relative size or distance.

The Earliest Units

Man has always been concerned with measuring. For body covering the cave man compared his own size with that of an animal skin. The skin needed to be "big enough to cover him"; if it was "too small," it was discarded. Questions about "how long" and "how far" have concerned man since his earliest days on earth. Having no measuring devices and no standard, primitive man judged length and distance by eye or time, and each person worked individually establishing his own ways of measuring to meet his own needs. Man's first measuring guides were directly involved with himself and his possessions. The parts of his body served as units for measuring things: thumb, hand span, foot, arms outstretched, and so on. The physiognomic paradigm was as basic to the development of measurement as it was to systems of numeration.

An informational pamphlet about elementary school mathematics, published by the New York State Education Department, includes the chart shown as Table 6, describing early units of measure in terms of their human physical counterparts.

References to interrelationships of these measures are also noted in the pamphlet: A palm was equivalent to about four digits, a span to three palms, two spans to a cubit. Establishment of such relationships was aimed at developing a *system* of measurement.

Eventually one cut log served as a measure to get others the same size—and later thin sticks of varying sizes were cut to serve as measuring guides because they were easier to work with. Stones and containers were used to measure weight and capacity. These particular forms of measurement were governed by concepts of matching and substitution, and constituted a significant advance in measurement technique. It is evident, however, that such measures were still fairly gross approximations.

Mueller views the history of measurement as being basically a history not of ideas but of techniques in the development and use of units of measure: "Since continuous magnitudes present no logical breaks or subdivisions, the choice of a unit of measure is purely arbitrary, a matter of convenience to the user." [10]

Table 6

Derivation of Some Early Units of Measure

Name	Description	Approximate Value in Today's Units
Digit	Width of a finger	¾ inch
Palm	Width of a palm	3 inches
Span	From the tip of the thumb to the tip of the little finger of an outstretched hand	9 inches
Cubit	From the tip of the elbow to the end of the middle finger	1½ feet
Yard	From the tip of the nose to the end of the thumb of an outstretched hand	3 feet
Foot	Length of a man's foot	12 inches
Step	Length of a man's average step	2½ feet
Pace	Length of a man's double step	5 feet
League	Distance a person could see from the shore	3 miles

SOURCE: SUNY, *Geometry and Measurement* (1965), p. 16.

Services to Commerce and Trade

In precivilized eras men moved from place to place hunting food. As populations grew, people turned to staying within one area and farming. The development of agriculture led to many measurement needs: determining areas, setting boundary lines, and planning the building of houses. As towns and cities developed, some form of government was required, and this led to taxes to support the government. The problem of taxes involved many new measurement needs. Before money, taxes were in the form of grain or cloth or livestock, and these needed to be measured. Later, when metals were discovered and used in trade, even more accuracy in measurement was required.

"Even in modern times, we are still refining our measurements," says Isaac Asimov:

> And although the world's nations quarrel so desperately that it would seem they could never agree on anything, all have been honestly cooperating in the establishment of international systems of measurement.[11]

It is probably fair to say that there is a direct relationship between the extent of a given culture's commerce and the development of the measurement techniques of that culture. The greater the commerce, the more precise must measurement be.

The Need for Standardization

Whereas the ancients at first described measurements verbally, most often in terms of body units, by the time writing had developed so had the need to record such measurements as property and tax assessments. Once it was recognized that a very long distance could be measured by matching a length of cloth with the length of a man's arm and then seeing how many times the cloth could be placed along that distance to give a total number of arm lengths, the specialized techniques of arithmetic were already being applied to measurement.[12]

Although the body units provided convenient ways for measuring lengths, at some point people unquestionably became concerned with the fact that a "foot" could vary in size depending upon whose foot it was! These differences in physical size led to a recognition that a generally agreed-upon length for certain sizes would be enormously helpful for accurate communication and would eliminate, to a large extent, the possibility of being "shortchanged."

From that point on, the idea of standard measures grew and different units were established. The measures themselves evolved directly from practical needs of people engaged in particular occupations. This fact gives the measures the advantage of being readily convenient dimensions. At a later point in history the government legalized, usually by royal decree, the measure that was already in wide use.

Early Standard Measures:
Length, Weight, Time

Perhaps understanding of how current standard measures evolved may be most easily grasped through studying the origins of early standard units of length, weight, and time and the terms that represented them. The word *unit* itself, given to all the different types of measure, comes from the latin *unus*, meaning "one."

Length. Of beginnings in this connection, Copeland says:

> One of the first standard units of measure was the cubit, which was defined as the distance from a man's elbow to the tip of his middle finger. The cubit was used by the Egyptians as a unit of measure as early as 2600 B.C. The cubit varied slightly in length from country to country.[13]

And from Osborn:

> The inch [from the Latin *uncia*, meaning one-twelfth] originally established by the Romans as a twelfth of a foot measure, was declared by King David of Scotland to be the average width of the thumbs of a small, middle size, and large man. In England, King Edward II decreed

that the inch was to be the length of 3 barley corns, and 12 barley corn inches were to make a foot, and 3 such feet were to make a yard.[14]

The length of a man's foot was the original standard for the present *foot* measure, the width of his thumb was once the standard *inch*, and the *yard* was originally a Saxon measure for the distance around a man's body at chest level. This yard was also the length from finger tip of the outstretched arm, or about half a fathom. *Fathom* comes from an Anglo-Saxon word meaning "embrace," and involves the full length of the outstretched arms. For long distances the Roman words *mille passum*, "one thousand paces," represented approximately 5,000 feet (one *pace* was about five feet) in length; hence the English *mile*, 5280 feet. And the term *furlong*, used today mainly in horse-racing, comes from *furrow long*, referring to the length of a furrow that an ox could plow without a rest. Eventually it was standardized at forty rods.

As a unit of linear measure, the *rod* has an interesting story connecting the past with the present. It was originally a stick which a plowman used both as an ox goad and as an aid in measuring certain distances. Presently standardized at sixteen and a half feet, it stems from a sixteenth-century German rule establishing a relationship between the foot and the rod:

> If you stand at the door of a church on Sunday, and have sixteen men stop—tall ones and short ones—as they leave after service and have them stand so that their left feet are toe to heel behind each other, the length obtained shall be the right and lawful *rod* with which to measure and survey land. Furthermore, the sixteenth part of that distance shall be the right and lawful *foot*.[15]

Weight. The current *pound* measure of weight can be traced to an ancient Greek silver coin. The name of this coin, *litra*, was also the word for "pound." (The modern word *liter*, for the basic unit of capacity in the metric system, actually derives from the Greek *litra*.) The current abbreviation for pound, *lb.*, comes from the Latin *libra*, meaning "pound," and the word *pound* itself is derived from the Latin *pondus*, meaning "weight."

In the Europe of medieval times there was an endless variety of pounds, none of them having any widespread acceptance as a standard measure. The Troy pound of twelve *ounces* (from the Latin *uncia*) originated in Troyes, France, and began to be used in England in the thirteenth century. However, by the sixteenth century the Troy measure was replaced by the avoirdupois pound of sixteen ounces. The avoirdupois pound, employed for larger and bulkier measures, was a cheaper and more convenient standard weight to manufacture. The word *avoirdupois* itself comes from medieval French words meaning "to have weight." For minute weights of precious metals, like gold and silver, Troy measure is still used today. The English monetary pound, which originally meant a pound of silver, was also based on the Troy system of measurement.

Of the *grain*, basis for various measures of weight, Cajori writes:

> The history of measures of weight brings out the curious fact that among the Hindus and Egyptians, as well as Italians, English and other Europeans, the basis for the unit of weight lay usually in the *grain of barley*. This was also a favorite unit of length. The lowest subdivision of the pound, or of other similar units, was usually defined as weighing the same as a certain number of grains of barley. That no great degree of accuracy could be secured and maintained on such a basis is evident.[16]

Time. The measurement of time also has its own characteristic history. Early man judged time by the sun—by the length of time it took in its daily and yearly cycles, and by the length and angles of the shadows it cast. Early estimates of time were made on the basis of shadows cast by sticks.

The ancient Babylonians had noted that it took the sun 365 days to complete its yearly cycle, and the circular nature of its "orbit" had long been observed. By the year 3000 B.C. the Babylonians had divided the year into 360 days, even though they had noted the actual 365-day period. They used 360 rather than 365 because of the fact that 365 has only two divisors (5 and 73), whereas 360 has twenty-two divisors. It was the ancient Sumerians and Egyptians who divided the day into 24 hours.

The notion of a 24-hour period comprising both day and night, however, is a sufficiently late development that many languages lack a proper word for it:

> Some primitive peoples use such expressions as "light and darkness," "sun–darkness". . . . But this is rare. The days are counted according to the *pars-pro-toto* method in "suns," "nights," "sleeps," "dawns" (Homer); whoever has slept six nights on the way has undertaken a six days' journey. The counting in nights was especially favoured by the old Teutonic peoples (*cf.* the expressions "fortnight," "sennight").[17]

Early sundials were calibrated so that the length of an hour could be judged, but these of course could be used only on sunny days. The ancients also estimated the interval of one hour by the length of time it took to burn a candle or a segmented length of rope.

The earliest timer consisted of water pouring from a jar, causing a marker to turn on a disk. Later there was the hourglass, which was based on the interval it took for a given amount of sand to pass from one bulb into another—this interval being made to correspond to the twenty-fourth part of a day.

About nine hundred years ago the first clocks were devised. These clocks had no face but contained a figure which would jump up, or bells which would ring, every hour. Later, the face was added, as were hands, and springs were used to supply mechanical force. Electricity eventually supplanted mechanical force in a large number of clocks, and today there are battery-operated clocks and even some electronic ones. The standard measure of time in the United States is supplied by the Naval Observatory in Washington, D.C. In the future it is likely that standard time will be determined by atomic clocks, which will keep time more exactly than ever before. Such measures are already being used in space travel.

The units of time—days, hours, and seconds—are based on a natural standard recognized through the ages: the rotation of the earth, which is almost perfectly constant. Units of length and weight vary considerably from culture to culture; but all the civilized world agrees on the units of time.

Achieving Uniformity of Standards

History shows that ancient cultures had established standard units for various measures such as weight, length, and capacity, and for astronomy with respect to the calendar and navigation. Evidence of mathematical skill as well as accurate measurement is found in Egyptian and Babylonian civilizations in such engineering achievements as temples and pyramid structures; and Greek geometric and trigonometric theories and applications reflect vastly greater sophistication.[18]

At the time of the American Revolution, the measures used in the colonies were of course the same as those of Great Britain. Far from having any scientific basis, these measures were greatly lacking in uniformity. Although the problem was generally recognized, it was many years before action was taken.

An investigation sponsored by the Senate in 1830 revealed large discrepancies among the weights and measures in use in the principal customhouses. As a result, progress in establishing uniform standards was made in the United States, with the yard of 36 inches, the avoirdupois pounds of 7,000 grains, the wine gallon of 231 cubic inches, and the Winchester bushel of 2,150.42 cubic inches.[19] These units are still operative in the United States today.

From need and through experience, measures have been selected and modified over the centuries, the general direction being toward greater accuracy and precision. Yet with all of civilization's efforts toward more exacting communication in terms of measurement, even in this present scientific age there exists surprising lack of uniformity in some standard measures.

Mueller describes chaotic conditions within the United States with respect to dry measures:

> Not only does the bushel differ in capacity for such diverse items as charcoal, corn, and potatoes, but the bushel also varies from one part of the country to another. It is reported that there are eight kinds of tons and nine different volumes for barrel; the U.S. National Bureau of Standards uses over 500 pages of fine type to define all units of measures extant.[20]

And differences of various kinds exist not only within the United States but also between countries. For example, the United States defines its wine gallon by volume and the British define theirs by weight. Consequently the two are not exactly interchangeable. Another difference between the measurement systems of these two countries is the fact that in the United States the interchange of dry measure and liquid measure units is not legal, whereas in England there are specified relationships.

Mueller comments that "the outstanding fact in the history of weights and measures in the United States and England is that the basic units are personal in origin and traditional in maintenance. . . . The most remarkable thing about the decimalized [metric] system is the fact that it is based entirely upon science and logic and represents a clean break from custom." [21]

The metric system originated in France in the late eighteenth century, and today every major nation except the United States either uses it fully, is in the process of converting to it, or is planning a conversion program. Further, only eight small developing countries have yet to start metrication.

The system has as its basic unit of length the *meter*, which by definition is the distance between two marks on a platinum bar deposited in the Archives of the State of France. Mueller explains that at the time the measure was devised, in 1799, this length represented "the best estimate of one ten-millionth part of a terrestrial meridian running through Paris and stretching between the equator and the north pole." [22] The meter is equal to 39.37 U.S. inches. The basic unit for volume is the *liter*, which is a little more than a quart: .2462 U.S. gallon. The basic unit for weight, the *gram*, is approximately .035 ounce, with 1,000 grams equal to 2.2 pounds.

Since 1866, the metric system has been recognized in the United States as *one* legal means of measurement. In other countries it is the *only* legal system. At the present time, it is widely used here by the National Aeronautics and Space Administration, the U.S. military services, and the pharmaceutical, optical, chemical, and electronic industries.

A *New York Times* news item of 30 July 1971 (page 13) reports on the just-completed, two-and-one-half-year, $2.5 million study of the United States National Bureau of Standards, which strongly recommends that this country become fully metric.[23] In support of this recommendation is the opinion of experts that billions of dollars would be gained in overseas trade which are now lost through costly conversions between the two systems, and also their belief that increasing world-wide technology necessitates adopting the language of measurement used almost universally. Predictions are that 90 per cent of world trade will be in metric terms within twenty years. A distinct advantage to the United States in starting to adopt metrication (as noted by Dr. Lewis M. Branscomb, director of the Bureau of Standards, in the *Times*) is the opportunity to participate with other industrial nations now in the process of devising an international set of industrial standards of weights and measures.

On the same date, in a *New York Post* article entitled "Going Metric" (page 30), Sylvia Porter responds to the question: What does this mean to you and me? She says:

> Among other things, virtually every package would be redesigned and relabeled. Gone would be proper and improper fractions, least common denominators, troy and avoirdupois ounces. Sewing materials would be sold by the meter and all dress patterns and sizes would be changed.
>
> Fahrenheit would turn to centigrade with the freezing point at a sensible zero and the boiling point at 100 degrees. All school books at all levels would be revised, so would speed limit signs and speedometers. So would rulers, scales, etc., etc.

Although it is often said that the U.S. system of weights and measures is far more complex and difficult to learn than the metric system, it is also known that a society long accustomed to using particular weights and measures will encounter considerable difficulty in changing to another system—even to one recognized as being superior and easier to learn.

The following points are offered as a helpful start to grasping the concept of the metric system:

1. The three basic units—the *meter* for length, the *gram* for weight, the *liter* for volume—have multiples and subdivisions following a ratio of 1:10. (Note that this makes the system particularly compatible with the decimal system of numeration.)

2. Greek prefixes indicate the multiples: *deca*, for ten; *hecto*, for hundred; *kilo*, for thousand; *myria*, for ten thousand. That is:

1 decameter = 10 meters
1 hectometer = 100 meters
1 kilometer = 1,000 meters
1 myriameter = 10,000 meters

Latin prefixes indicate the subunits: *deci*, for tenths; *centi*, for hundredths; *milli*, for thousandths. That is:

1 decimeter = .1 meter
1 centimeter = .01 meter
1 millimeter = .001 meter

The same prefixes are used to designate the number of grams or liters. For example, 1 kilogram (1,000 grams); 1 deciliter (.1 liter).

It follows, then, that if the meter is equal to 39.37 inches, 1 decameter is equal to 393.7 inches. 1 decimeter is equal to 3.937 inches, and so on. This is a useful way of making comparisons between the systems. However, when one need no longer depend upon the idea of equivalency in inches, the necessary shift in thinking within one framework to thinking in another has been achieved and freedom within the new system gained. Perhaps the most important initial step in this direction is to "get the feel of" these new units in the same way one has a "feel" for an inch or a foot. A part of one's thumb is often used as an approximation for an inch. Establishing a similar aid for, say, a centimeter or a decimeter might be one's personal key to clarifying and effectively using the metric system.

The concept of measurement has grown over more than five thousand years, from measuring simple lengths to calculating the units of measure for 250,000 pounds of thrust for a missile lift-off. Standard units of measure are defined by law but have their origins in widespread use and acceptance of the people. Through the ages man has constantly sought to increase the accuracy of measurement. And although measurement is concerned with the concrete, man's concern with it, as Rappaport has pointed out, has often led to the growth of mathematics itself:

> His interest in measurement led to the development of fractions, which resulted in the development of rational numbers. Newton developed the calculus when he tried to calculate the gravitational pull of the earth upon a physical body. Applied mathematics has often led to the development of abstract mathematics.[24]

IMPLICATIONS FOR EDUCATION

The significance of measurement in the school curriculum is difficult to exaggerate. Even as history in its own right, the field of measurement as it has developed from times of antiquity has an undoubted fascination. The concepts of measurement, as these apply to science as well as to commerce and the history of man's thinking, present an infinitely rich resource to teachers and to students.

As with the development of numeration systems, it must be recognized that a measurement unit or system is a product of man's thinking and efforts, not any sort of self-evident or ready-made or divinely ordained instrument. Each type of measurement, as well as each unit of measurement, has a unique history and significance in terms of the challenges and needs which have beet met.

Measurement is a phenomenon which permeates every facet of modern living. It is basic to the construction of modern buildings, the weighing of groceries, the regulation of distances in sporting events, the monetary systems of the world, and the exploration of space. These and very many more uses of measurement may all be explored within the classroom.

Traditionally, the topic of measurement has been given attention in elementary school curriculum. Perhaps it is the only one of the six concepts explored in this study that has generally been handled in a way that allows the student some degree of "trying things out" in the classroom setting. Present knowledge and emphases call for an extension of such participatory experience. Challenged through carefully sequenced questions to find ways of determining length, width, weight, or time of day without the currently available instruments, students may re-experience centuries of history in a brief period, provided that sufficient time is allowed for reflecting upon the problems, experimenting with possible alternatives, and carrying on appropriate discussion. Such an approach encourages individual creativeness, sharpens a student's understanding of the concept of measurement, and helps him to grasp the significance of key ideas.

Perhaps most important of these ideas are those of precision, objective observation, and standardized recording of data, which are implicit in all modern measurement. Involved participation in experiences which center upon these concepts conveys to the student the importance of precision in his own thinking and deepens his appreciation of the significance of the concepts to the development of modern science.

SIX

Geometry

IDEAS AND SHAPES

It has been said that the nineteenth century has produced five times as much mathematics as all the previous centuries combined. The prediction for the close of the twentieth century is that more mathematics will have been developed during those one hundred years than the total contribution preceding that time [1]—a staggering thought with profound implications for educational programs!

This phenomenal growth in the field of mathematics, along with concomitant applications in science, engineering, and particularly space technology, has made it imperative that the study of geometry—a prominent branch of mathematics—no longer be left until the second year of high school.

Through recent curriculum reforms, some geometric concepts are now given considerable attention throughout the elementary grades, in many instances starting with the kindergarten. There is, however, an important distinction between the formal geometry of the tenth grade and the informal geometry which is part of the new approach in elementary school programs. Formal geometry employs deductive reasoning and logical proofs. It starts with certain undefined terms and statements (axioms or postulates) about these terms which are accepted as true without requiring proof. Informal geometry emphasizes the properties of familiar objects. It focuses on such mathematical ideas as points, lines, planes, angles, and space. Children may observe models of these forms in their environment; and by means of measurement, experimentation, intuition, and inductive reasoning, generalizations are discovered. This form of geometric discovery is often referred to as intuitive geometry.

Commenting on the inadequacy of the conventional one year of geometry in the tenth grade, Brune notes:

> Informal geometry in the elementary grades can, therefore, counteract a serious deficiency. In these grades geometry is the study of form. Shapes, sizes, patterns, designs—these are the stuff from which children form concepts. From studying forms children discover numerous geometric relations; from making constructions pupils learn about geometric facts; from measuring figures learners acquire a background of geometric information. The work teems with both classical concepts and contemporary concepts.[2]

It is not possible within the context of this study to trace the history of geometry in any great detail. It is a very long history, and a large part of it is neither appropriate to the education of grade school students nor particularly necessary as part of the background of their teachers. In many instances, highly sophisticated knowledge of the subject matter of geometry is required in order fully to appreciate the path of its development.

The following material is, therefore, concerned only with selected developmental aspects which might enhance teachers' understanding and appreciation of this branch of mathematics and ultimately be of value to children in the grades.

GEOMETRY AND MEASUREMENT

The beginnings of geometry, like the beginnings of the concepts of numeration and measurement, go back to man's basic experiences in living, and those encountered in primitive times have been lost in antiquity. As noted earlier, the ancient Egyptian and Babylonian temples and pyramids showed considerable architectural knowledge and precision of measurement. In these structures, as well as in other aspects of these two cultures, the application of geometric principles is clearly evident.

It is likely that the blueprints of those times were in the form of clay tablets. The builders certainly knew that two things differing in size may have exactly the same shape [3]—a fundamental geometric principle.

Three examples of geometric measurements known and used by the ancients and appropriate for elementary and intermediate school curriculum are discussed here with respect to the needs which led to their development.

Right-Angle Measurement

It is obvious that there were innumerable instances which called for right-angle measurement in Egyptian architecture. Right angles can be constructed by drawing equal intersecting arcs from any two points on a straight line and connecting the points where the arcs intersect. (See the example below.) Probably the early builders learned to do this, drawing lines on the ground and using string and pegs to find the arc intersections.[4]

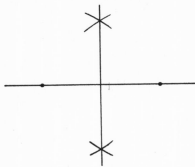

At that time one way of determining linear measurement was by equally spaced knots in rope. Hogben speculates that it is possible that the professional rope knotters discovered that "pegging out certain lengths of rope [3, 4, and 5, for example] in the form of a triangle produces a right angle opposite the largest side."[5] A wood model of such triangles then provides a set-square, the simple tool eventually developed by the ancients to meet this measurement need.

Gow, raising the question as to what first led man to examine the properties of geometric form, cites Herodotus' account of Egyptian land having to be divided into rectangular or square plots for taxation purposes, and the appointment of surveyors to assess tax reduction where land was swept away by the annual flooding of the Nile. Such land measurements, he conjectures, had to do with periphery. Then, in due time, as areas of one shape were exchanged for areas of another shape, it was discovered that shapes with equal periphery did not necessarily have the same area. "A discovery of this kind," he adds, "would at once call attention to angles and suggest the propriety of establishing a unit of area."[6] A somewhat different notion of how measurement for area may have developed follows.

Area of a Rectangle

The priests of early Egypt received compensation for their services from taxes paid by farmers in the form of goods. The amount of the tax was determined by the size of the farm, so it was necessary to have a measurement for area. Square tiles used for covering floors may well have provided the first clue to solving this problem.[7] A floor three tiles long and five tiles wide needed fifteen tiles (3×5) to cover it; a floor seven tiles long and six tiles wide needed forty-two tiles (7×6). In general, then, the area to be covered could be found by multiplying its length by its width.

Area of a Triangle

Some farm land could not be divided into rectangular sections, but in many instances the priests found that it could be divided into triangles.[8] No doubt it was soon recognized that any square or other rectangle can be divided into two right triangles each of which is half the area of the rectangle, and that any triangle may be divided into two right triangles each of which is half the area of a rectangle determined by the base and height of the right triangle. Thus it was possible to find the area of any triangle by multiplying its base by its height and dividing the answer by two.

The yearly overflow of the Nile contributed to the growth of good crops but also washed away boundary lines between farms, making the measuring of fields a job to be done over and over again. Hogben describes the priests of Egypt as not only calendar-makers and architects but also the first professional surveyors.[9] In fact, their problems of measuring land and restoring boundaries in flooded areas are frequently cited as the point at which geometric ideas took root; and their practical learnings about the shapes and areas of triangles also contributed much to the work of later mathematicians.

A SELECTIVE HISTORY

Historically speaking, geometry and arithmetic have grown side by side, merging in what is generally called metric geometry—number applied as measures to geometric form.[10] The word *geometry* is of Greek origin and means measurement of the earth (derived from *ge,* meaning "earth," and *metrein,* "to measure"), and appropriately so, since its earliest applications were concerned with earth measurement. Webster defines geometry as "that branch of mathematics which investigates the relations, properties, and measurements of solids, surfaces, lines, and angles; the science that treats of the properties and relations of spatial magnitudes; the theory of space and figures in space." This definition reflects man's work from earliest times to the present in developing the science of geometry. Some of the factors which influenced this definition—and its clarity and precision—may be seen in the selected historical matter that follows. (The classification of periods follows that of the *Encyclopaedia Britannica.*)

Ancient Empirical Geometry

That the origin of geometry was intuitive is cited by various mathematical historians. Smith, for example, says: "It [early geometry] sought facts relating to mensuration without attempting to demonstrate these facts by any process of deductive reasoning." [11] He characterizes this period, which he refers to as that of "prehistoric geometry," as one which was primarily concerned with agreeable forms such as the interwoven symmetric figures in a mat.

In the next stage of geometry, also largely empirical, measurement of rectangles and triangles was the major concern, although according to Gow the Egyptians calculated the solid contents of barns before measuring areas.[12] Gow's designation for this whole early period is "Prehistoric and Egyptian Geometry." Among the interesting observations he makes about geometry's beginnings is that the human body did not provide any suitable unit of area or solid measure, whereas the palm, the hand span, the foot, and other bodily parts had readily served as units of length. For distances, measured in terms of human capacity, there were the phrases "a stone's throw," "within shouting distance," and "a day's journey" to communicate approximately "how far" or "how long." Similarly, large areas or volumes were sometimes referred to in terms of human labor: "a morning's work" or "a day's work." [13]

The Ahmes papyrus (Egyptian, c. 1650 b.c.), the most important of known ancient mathematical manuscripts, has been described and interpreted by a number of historians, including Gow (1884) and Cajori (1896). It deals in part with the areas of various figures—squares, rectangles, circles, trapezoids, and one isosceles triangle. In problems relating to the building of pyramids, there is evidence of some knowledge of similarity of figures in terms of related proportions. With regard to the area of a circle, an interesting rule was used: "From the diameter subtract one-ninth of it, and square the remainder," which indicates that pi was figured as approximately 3.16—a reasonably good approximation for those times.

Certain errors have been identified in Ahmes's figures. For instance, Cajori refers to Ahmes's example Number 51, in which the area of an isosceles triangle whose sides are 10 and whose base is 4 is stated to be 20. Ahmes arrived at this answer by taking the product of one side and half the base.[14] The correct value, 19.6, is found by taking one-half the product of the base and the height of the triangle.

Historians have noted the extreme care the Egyptians gave to the exact location of their temples. To accomplish their objectives it was necessary to obtain accurate north-south and east-west lines. "By observing the points on the horizon where a star rose and set, and taking a plane midway between them, they could obtain a north and south line." [15] To this line an east-west line was then drawn at right angles by employing a rope stretched around three pegs to form a right triangle with sides in the proportion 3:4:5.

The Greek philosopher Democritus (c. 460–370 B.C.) is quoted as saying: "In the construction of plane figures . . . no one has yet surpassed me, not even the so-called 'Harpedonaptoe' of Egypt." [16] *Harpedonaptoe* is made up of two Greek words meaning "rope-stretchers." Cajori credits Moritz Cantor—"prince of mathematical historians" of the nineteenth century—with drawing attention to the etymology of this word and using the clue along with others as evidence of this Egyptian practice in laying out their temples.[17]

Although Egyptian geometry was completely practical in nature, considerable time, observation, thought, and experimentation are implied in this development of applied mathematics. One might wonder why the people who invented so much practical geometry did not continue to make further discoveries and thus develop a science of geometry. Gow reports that the priests of Egypt were leaders in land surveying, writing, medicine, and other practical arts. As slaves of tradition, they were afraid to make changes in rules or to extend knowledge in their craft, and geometry was treated accordingly.[18] And, Cajori says: "Their discoveries in mathematics, and in medicine, were entered at an early time upon their sacred books, and . . . in after ages it was considered heretical to modify or augment anything therein. Thus the books themselves closed the gates to progress." [19]

All this notwithstanding, the records of history are clear as to "the universal testimony of Greek writers that Greek geometry was, in the first instance, derived from Egypt, and that the latter country remained for many years afterwards the chief source of mathematical teaching." [20] To the Egyptians the world owes the first steps in geometry.

From the Babylonians, the Chinese, and the Indians, the tablets handed down include many problems involving mensuration, all largely empirical, with no evidence of deductive reasoning. Cajori mentions a Babylonian text having the Sumerian word *tim,* meaning "line" and (originally) "rope," and suggests that this accounts for the conjecture that the Babylonians, like the Egyptians, used ropes for measuring distances and angles.[21] He also cites the Babylonian sign $*$, seen in a drawing of the wheel spokes of a royal carriage, as having relationship to the Babylonian division of the circle into six equal parts.

The Romans used geometry intuitively and for its practical value in measuring land, planning cities, and engineering warfare,[22] but the science of geometry held no interest for the Romans. Empirical rules and approximate formulas satisfied their architectural needs.[23]

Ancient Demonstrative Geometry

Following the period of ancient empirical geometry was that of ancient demonstrative geometry, initiated by the Greeks and developed by them for more than one thousand years. Its beginnings are rooted in the work of Thales (640–546 B.C.), which emerged from the empirical stage and demonstrated the proof of six theorems.[24]

Thales presented a geometry of lines and angles, as compared with the Egyptian geometry of areas and volumes. As was common among the Greek scholars of the seventh century B.C., Thales traveled to Egypt to receive instruction from the priests. His speculative and analytic mind extended the Egyptian everyday mathematical applications to include a view of how things are related, thus leading the way in the development of a science of geometry. Thales treated such relationships as the equality of vertical angles and of the base angles of an isosceles triangle, and the bisection of a circle by its diameter.[25]

Thales is also reported to have measured the heights of pyramids by the length of their shadows, thus implying an understanding of proportionality of the sides of similar triangles. Historians differ, however, as to his method and the actual knowledge he acquired. Proclus's abstract of a lost history of geometry written by Eudemus, a pupil of Aristotle, is considered a reliable source. Referred to by Cajori as the *Eudemian Summary*, it credits Thales with the theorem that two triangles are congruent if they have a side and two adjacent angles equal respectively. Thales may have applied this theorem to calculate the distance of ships from shore.[26] Gow, however, considers it more probable that Thales used the proposition "that the sides of equiangular triangles are proportional" to determine ship-to-shore distances.[27]

"The transition from empirical to rigorous demonstrative geometry was necessarily very slow," says Cajori. The discovery by Pythagoreans in Italy of the existence of incommensurable magnitudes (such as the side and diagonal of a square) marks a long step toward reasoned conclusions."[28] Pythagoras (c. 572–501 B.C.) is said to have been a pupil of Thales. Information about his life is limited, and for a long period of his lifetime there is no record of his whereabouts. Cajori believes that the evidence points to his having been born in Samos. It is thought that he traveled and studied abroad (particularly in Egypt), and it is known that he was influenced by and contributed to an era characterized by much significant thinking and writing.

After years of journeying, Pythagoras established his School of Crotona in southeastern Italy (called Magna Graecia, "Great Greece," by the Italian Greeks) for the well-to-do young men in that location. He classified his disciples as either "hearers" or "mathematicians," the latter first having been members of the former group. Only to the "mathematicians" did Pythagoras reveal his learnings, and they were pledged to secrecy regarding this knowledge. Smith believes that this brotherhood has ever since served as a model for all the secret societies in Europe and America.[29]

Since the discoveries of the Pythagorean school were always ascribed to its founder, the identification of particular members of the school with the development of specific mathematical knowledge has never been determined.[30] Pythagoras left no mathematics treatises, and all but a few fragments of Philolaus's detailed publication (c. 400 B.C.) of Pythagorean philosophy are lost.[31] It is, therefore, largely through the references of later writers that his work is known. And, whereas there is considerable evidence that Pythagoras made geometry an outstanding Greek science, little in the way of particulars can be ascribed either to him or to his early followers.

In this science, Pythagoras is credited with having defined a point as "unity having position" and, in fact, with having been the first to use definitions in mathematical work. There is some evidence that he proved the proposition that the sum of the angles of a triangle is 180 degrees, that he constructed both congruent and similar polygons, and that he viewed the earth as a sphere in space.[32] In the summary of the lost Eudemus history of Greek geometry, Proclus credits Pythagoras with the discovery of incommensurable quantities.[33] Whether Pythagoras actually proved the theorem to which his name became attached has never been firmly established.

According to Kline's account, in *Mathematics and the Physical World*, both the Pythagorean Theorem and the idea of incommensurable quantities grew out of the Pythagorean analysis of numbers, which involved classifying numbers in terms of certain shapes in which certain numbers of dots (or other tallying marks) could be arranged.[34] For example:

No doubt the students of Crotona often performed such analyses with pebbles or by markings in the sand. (In any case, their only prior experience with number symbols would have been with primitive Roman numerals not more than a step or two removed from a one-for-one tallying procedure.)

The numbers 3, 6, 10, and so on, were represented in the form of triangles and referred to as "triangular numbers." And "square numbers" was the term given to 4, 9, 16, and so on. Modern terminology still reflects this Pythagorean emphasis, in that "to the second power" is rarely used, the term "squared" being preferred.

These geometrical arrangements made visible some of the properties of whole numbers. For example, as shown in the illustration below, a diagonal divided a square number into two triangular numbers. This led the Pythagoreans to conclude that the sum of two consecutive triangular numbers is always a square number. (When the progression representing triangular numbers is extended, this fact is more easily recognized: 3, 6, 10, 15, 21, 28 . . . .) They also discovered that adding a "gnomon" to a square number resulted in the next square number. The gnomon, a carpenter's square, has the shape of the dots added to the second and third square numbers in the illustration.

This discovery may be expressed algebraically as follows: $n^2 + 2n + 1 = (n+1)^2$.

The Pythagoreans also associated numbers with natural and social concepts.[35] "One" was identified with reason, "two" with opinion because it suggested diversity, "four" with justice because it was the first product of equals. ("One" was not considered a number in the usual sense, since it represented unity.) The word *square* is of course still associated with the notion of justice, as in "square shooter" and "square deal."

A numerical relationship that fascinated the Pythagoreans was that of the sum of certain pairs of square numbers being also a square,[36] the classic example being $3^2 + 4^2 = 5^2$, that is, $9 + 16 = 25$. "Pythagorean triples" is the name still used for numbers having this relationship.

The famous Pythagorean Theorem—the square of the hypotenuse of a right triangle is equal to the sum of the squares of the legs (or sides)—stems from the Pythagorean triples relationship.[37] Two illustrations are shown:

$3^2 + 4^2 = 5^2$

$9 + 16 = 25$

$12^2 + 35^2 = 37^2$

$144 + 1225 = 1369$

Kline's account indicates that this same numerical relationship of triples led to the Pythagorean discovery of irrational numbers.[38] He believes that it occurred to a Pythagorean to examine the simplest case of the geometric theorem: a right triangle with sides each one unit in length. The sum of the squares is the square of the hypotenuse, which would then be 2. It was clear that 2 is not a square of any whole number and that $1 + 1 = 2$ is not a Pythagorean triple. The question as to whether $\sqrt{2}$ was perhaps a fraction was explored and eventually answered in the negative.

This was startling to the Pythagoreans. "Their entire philosophy of nature, which was based on the principle that every phenomenon could be reduced to whole numbers, was threatened." [39] To this new number element they gave the name "irrational," which at that time meant unmentionable or unknowable. (Today an "irrational number" is one which cannot be expressed as a ratio of whole numbers.) "There is a legend that the discovery of $\sqrt{2}$ was made by a member while the entire group of Pythagoreans was on a ship at sea. The member was thrown overboard and the rest of the group pledged to secrecy." [40]

In time, the Greeks accepted the fact that they had a new kind of number and they broadened their concept of number to include irrationals. Although irrationals were discovered by the Pythagoreans, it was not until the middle of the eighteenth century that mathematicians acknowledged irrational quantities in their proper perspective as useful elements of the number system.[41] The further development of irrationals as a significant mathematical idea is not indicated here.

"Pythagoras changed the study of geometry into the form of a liberal education," said Proclus, "for he examined its principles to the bottom and investigated its theorems in an immaterial and intellectual manner." [42] And Jourdain appraises the influence of Pythagoras in comparison with that of Thales: whereas Thales's major contribution to the science of geometry was that of deductive proof, Pythagoras changed it into an abstract science.[43]

Like Pythagoras, Plato (c. 440–349 B.C.) traveled extensively for the purpose of learning. It is thought that his contact with the Pythagoreans led to his interest in geometry. The value of his philosophical writings is a matter of record and not related to the focus of this book. Of the relationship between Plato's philosophy and mathematics, a quotation from the *Eudemian Summary* says: "He filled his writings with mathematical discourses, and exhibited on every occasion the remarkable connexion between mathematics and philosophy." [44] Of his work in furthering the science of geometry, it is said that Plato established its foundations through adherence to accurate definitions (such as for "point," "line," and "surface"), explicit assumptions, and logical proof.[45] That he invented the method of proof by analysis is cited by Proclus.[46]

The definition of a line as "breadthless length" is thought to have originated in the Platonian School. Plato himself defined the straight line as "that of which the middle covers the ends." Heath believes that this is what Euclid tried to say in defining a straight line as "a line which lies evenly with the points on it." [47]

The circle was defined by Plato as "that in which the farthest points in all directions are at the same distance from the middle (centre)," [48] and a Platonian axiom frequently referred to by Aristotle is: "If equals be taken from equals the remainders are equals." [49]

Plato's contributions to geometry were not in the form of original discoveries, but in the improvement of methods. Accurate definitions of geometric terms and clearly stated postulates and axioms had their beginnings in the work of Plato and were later adopted by Euclid.[50]

The School of Alexandria, the greatest of all ancient mathematics centers, flourished from around 300 B.C. to around A.D. 500. The most illustrious name associated with this school was that of Euclid. According to Cajori, it was during the period 330–320 B.C. that Euclid's *Elements* was written.[51] The *Elements* consisted of thirteen books, nine of which were devoted to geometry. The work is noted for its highly systematic treatment of the geometric knowledge developed up to that time. It organizes that knowledge in terms of propositions proved by reference to previously stated definitions, axioms, and postulates.

Proclus, in the *Eudemian Summary*, offered this appraisal: "Euclid, who wrote the Elements . . . brought to irrefragable proof propositions which had been less strictly proved by his predecessors." [52] The most famous proof of the Pythagorean Theorem is credited to Euclid.

Smith says of Euclid: "He is the only man to whom there ever came or ever can come again the glory of having successfully incorporated in his own writings all the essential parts of the accumulated mathematical knowledge of his time." [53]

And Cajori writes: "It is one of the marvels in the history of mathematics that the *Elements*, written in the 4th century B.C., should have established and maintained itself as a text-book in geometry for over 2000 years." [54]

Little is known of Euclid's life. There is no definite information as to the place or date of his birth. He may have been a Greek, or an Egyptian who came to Greece to study.

An interesting etymological source is worthy of mention. The word *volume* comes from the Latin word for the parchment scrolls on which all treatises were written in Euclid's time; it derived from a Latin root meaning "to roll." The Greek word for parchment was *biblos*; and small scrolls such as would comprise the parts of a long work or a collection were called *biblia* (whence Bible), which we translate as "books." This is why the parts of long written works, especially if they are ancient or quasi-classical, are often referred to as "books" (Book XII of the *Iliad*, the thirteen books of Euclid's *Elements*).

Historians have noted differences in Euclid's *Elements* as compared with most other writings on geometry. Smith mentions that Euclid included no intuitive geometry upon which the logical could rest, used no algebra as such or exercises of any kind, and demonstrated the correctness of constructions before their use.[55]

Although Euclid was writing in or about the year 300 B.C., the oldest surviving manuscripts which deal with his *Elements* date from about A.D. 900, twelve hundred years later; and these present differing views of Euclid's work.[56]

It is possible to present here only a few of the definitions, axioms, and postulates generally credited to Euclid's *Elements*. Those that follow show, in part, the extent of progress in geometry at that time. They are given as they appear in *Lectures on Fundamental Concepts of Algebra and Geometry* (1911), by John Wesley Young.

DEFINITIONS
1. A *point* is that which has no parts.
2. A *line* is length without breadth.
3. A *straight line* is a line which lies evenly between two of its points.

Euclid referred to his axioms as "common conceptions of thought" or "common notions." There were probably five of these.

AXIOMS
1. Things equal to the same thing are equal to each other.
2. If equals be added to equals, the results are equal.
3. If equals be subtracted from equals, the results are equal.
4. The whole is greater than any one of its parts.
5. Things that coincide are equal.

Young presents the postulates in full as they appeared in the German text of Heiberg.

POSTULATES
1. It shall be possible to draw a straight line joining any two points.
2. A terminated straight line may be extended without limit in either direction.
3. It shall be possible to draw a circle with given center and through a given point.
4. All right angles are equal.
5. If two straight lines in a plane meet another straight line in the plane so that the sum of the interior angles on the same side of the latter straight line is less than two right angles, then the two straight lines will meet on that side of the latter straight line.

These definitions, anxioms, and postulates constituted the beginning point of Euclid's *Elements*. The axioms seem intended to represent basic notions of logic applicable to any science; the postulates, all geometric, suggest primitive propositions concerning space.[57]

The text of the *Elements* has been subject to considerable criticism by mathematicians over the ages. Some errors are thought to have been the result of poor editing, others to inaccuracies on the part of Euclid. As mathematical knowledge was extended, weaknesses in the

Elements were identified and subsequently corrected. However, the excellence of this work as a scientific treatise is universally recognized. In Kline's view, its major value lies in the evidence it supplies of "the power of human reason to derive new knowledge by deductive reasoning" and of "the rational and indeed mathematical design of nature." [58]

There were ancients both before and after Euclid who contributed to developing mathematics based on sound logic. Among those preceding Euclid was Socrates, usually not thought of as a mathematician, whose attention to inductive thinking and precise definitions constituted an important contribution to the development of logical geometry. His work influenced that of Plato and Euclid as well as others.

Among those who came after Euclid are such great scholars as Eratosthenes, one of whose mathematical achievements was that of measuring the circumference and diameter of the earth, and Archimedes, considered one of the most outstanding mathematicians and physicists of all time. Archimedes' (c. 287–212 B.C.) work in geometry consisted mainly of original research concerning theorems of quadrature and cubature which eventually led to the calculus of the infinite, discovered in turn and perfected by mathematicians of the seventeenth and eighteenth centuries. [59]

"In the history of mathematics, as in the history of civilization in general, it is the setting forth of a great idea that counts." Smith is referring here specifically to Thales's geometric propositions—intuitive statements so simple that they might seem unimportant, but the proof of which caused other mathematicians to note them in their own works. "Without Thales," he states, "there would not have been a Pythagoras— or such a Pythagoras; and without Pythagoras there would not have been a Plato—or such a Plato." [60]

The more general significance of Smith's point is that Euclid's systematization and treatment of the geometric knowledge developed to his time depended upon the quality of the thinking and achievements of his predecessors. This notion is particularly relevant to the concerns of this book. That is, each discoverer in science builds upon the ideas of his predecessors, and the history of science is thus a study of the sources and development of basic ideas. Most often these ideas originate in concrete observations related to practical human needs or necessities, and these observations later become elaborated in an abstract vein in such a way as to evolve into general scientific laws governing a broad scope of subject matter vital to human endeavor.

Later Periods

The development following the great period of Greek demonstrative geometry, in which Euclid played so large a part, has been classified by

Encylopaedia Britannica (1952) under the rubrics of Medieval Times and the Renaissance, The Invention of Analytic Geometry (17th century), Modern Synthetic Geometry (19th century), and Foundations of Geometry (late 19th century). In addition, *Britannica* provides an article on Non-Euclidian Geometry (19th century), which grew out of the questioning (from the time of the Greeks) of various assumptions— particularly the theory of parallels relating to Postulate 5 (see page 75) —which are the foundation of traditional Euclidean geometry.

The outstanding achievements of all these periods relate almost wholly to very complex ideas, such as (in the medieval time, for example) the geometric solution to cubic equations, an Arabic achievement. Treatment of the developmental roots and the growth of geometric ideas characteristic of these periods is, with one exception, beyond the limits of this investigation.

The exception is analytic geometry, which was formulated by Descartes and introduced in his *La géométrie* (1637). This invention constituted a highly significant step in the progress of mathematics. And, as Whitehead has pointed out, "The discovery of co-ordinate geometry, and also that of projective geometry about the same time, illustrate another fact which is being continually verified in the history of knowledge, namely, that some of the greatest discoveries are to be made among the most well-known topics." [61]

The two main ideas involved in analytic geometry are the location of points in a figure by the use of coordinates and the algebraic representation of a curve or surface by an equation involving two or three variables. These ideas, in simple form and application, are now part of most new elementary mathematics curricula.

Analytic geometry passed through three stages in its development: (1) the invention of a system of coordinates; (2) the recognition of one-to-one correspondence between algebra and geometry; and (3) the graphic representation of equations described by the expression $y = f(x)$.* Only the third step is modern. The first step has its roots in ancient Egyptian practices in laying out towns and fields, and in the early Greek use of latitude and longitude to locate points on earth and in the sky. Later, the Romans used a horizontal and a vertical axis, in a procedure comparable to the modern one, to arrange the streets of their towns. This was an improvement over the Egyptian grid-like figures used for the same purpose. [62]

---

* This expression is read "y is a function of x." It means that the changing values of one variable quantity, y, are determined by those of another, x, according to some rule (function), f, applied to x. For example, if the rule is that y is always 3 times x, then the equation expressing this is $y = 3x$. Thus if x is 1, y is 3; if x is 2, y is 6; and so on.

In the second stage, the relationship of algebra to geometry was probably at first no more than just a mathematician's mental recognition of an algebraic analogy to a geometric situation. In time, the algebraic works of various cultures began to show the use of geometric figures. In some cases Hindu algebraists gave two solutions to a problem, one algebraic and one geometric. Fibonacci, in *Practica geometriae* (1220) employed algebra in solving problems concerning the area of a triangle. He was the first prominent European mathematician to acknowledge the value of the relationship between algebra and geometry.[63]

Early books in print reflected the use of geometric figures in algebraic work. After publication (1545) of Cardan's *Ars Magna* (see also page 87), in which he used geometric figures in his solution to a cubic equation, the relationship between the two sciences came into fairly general use.[64]

By the seventeenth century, scientific and technological advances required work with such configurations as the ellipses, parabolas, and hyperbolas which are related to the paths of planets and comets. Other studies of curvature were concerned with the motion of the moon in relation to the location of ships at sea, with the lenses used for eyeglasses, telescopes and microscopes, and with the path of light rays through space.[65] Clearly, Euclid's geometry of straight lines and circles was no longer sufficient to serve man's growing needs.

Descartes's algebraic geometry provided a means of classifying and studying curves; it was referred to by John Stuart Mill as "the greatest single step ever made in the progress of the exact sciences." [66] (Historians acknowledge that Fermat was doing similar work independently, at the same time, but did not prepare his work for publication.)

Descartes used a coordinate system to show that every algebraic equation represents some geometric form and that for every geometric form there is an equation corresponding to it. With a coordinate system, sets of points in a plane can be described by the use of reference lines and numbers. Such a system is based on a one-to-one correspondence between a set of numbers and the set of points on a line. A rectangular coordinate system, the one commonly used in school programs, is one that employs reference lines that are perpendicular to each other.

The formulation of this relationship between algebra and geometry made it possible to study geometric figures, particularly curves, in a fashion far more precise than previously possible, and it opened the way to countless new and valuable applications, including those in space technology.

GEOMETRY'S RAPID GROWTH

This observation of Cajori's about early geometry is of special interest: "We suspect that our earliest records [of geometry] reaching back to about 2500 B.C. represent comparatively modern thought." [67]

If this be so, it is entirely reasonable to assume that advanced ideas in geometry would predate advanced ideas in other branches of mathematics. Perhaps the fact that geometric form is in the very nature of man's physical environment explains, in part, the earlier and more rapid pace of its development as a science.

In support of this view is Kline's response to the question of how the creators of geometry got to thinking about such things as perpendicularity, parallel lines, and congruent and similar figures. His answer is that "these basic relationships are all suggested by the observation of natural phenomena." [68] The tree is perpendicular to the ground, the river banks suggest parallel lines, the size and shape of different animals are their identifying characteristics. Geometric concepts, more easily visualized and represented graphically than those of arithmetic and algebra, thus provided the content for the first broad development of deductive reasoning in mathematics.

The more than one thousand theorems proved by the Greeks were based on a small number of axioms. And "the bridges and buildings designed in accordance with such theorems [still] hold up," observes Kline, citing this fact as strong evidence that "nature is designed in accordance with the rational pattern uncovered by Euclidean geometry." [69]

IMPLICATIONS FOR EDUCATION

Man's interest in simple geometric concepts—points, lines, planes, angles, and space—dates almost to the beginning of his existence. The concepts themselves embody basic geometric form, which is characteristic of everything that is part of man's environment—the stars, the moon, animals, trees, human beings, inanimate objects of all kinds.

Two comparisons between geometric ideas and other mathematical concepts are striking: (1) Whereas other mathematical ideas such as numeration and measurement systems were invented by man to meet his needs to deal with quantity and size, basic geometric forms—the circle, the triangle, the square—have always existed; they are a part of nature. Circular shape was seen in the sun, in the moon, and in man's eyes, triangular and square shapes in the patterns of the stars. (2) Mathematical ideas are, in general, encountered a considerable time after one's life has begun, but a person is exposed to geometric design from the day of his birth.

As an integral part of each person's daily existence from birth on, geometric form has a rightful place in the school curriculum. Just as the ancients explored form and the properties of form in the physical environment, so should the young student today examine the myriad objects in his physical setting to see of what they consist, to describe them in a variety of ways, to order the consequent information for relatedness to ideas within the discipline of mathematics and to other fields where possible.

In this process, meaning can be deepened through an awareness of the parallel investigations of men of earlier times. Even the errors found from time to time over the centuries in the works of the mathematicians have value. To try to retrace the steps in thinking that produced an error provides an enlightened view of the initial problem and heightens appreciation of a later more precise solution. This thread and others of practical value, the possibilities of new applications, and even the formation of new ideas are essential components in curriculum development and to the study of geometry in particular.

The implementation of such curriculum components will vary depending upon the maturity level of the child. But a teacher's knowledge of the roots of geometry and recognition of the significance of these threads may provide sound direction for the block-arranging of kindergartners, for the design-drawing of children in the middle grades, and for the more sophisticated scientific questions of upper-grade students.

SEVEN

Algebra

IDEAS AND SYMBOLS

Algebra—"the deeper waters of arithmetic" [1]—has also been called the "cornerstone of modern mathematics." [2] Many of its advanced developments have no direct relevance for the elementary curriculum; yet some of the most important elements of new mathematics programs derive from or connect directly with its concerns.

Understanding of the development of algebra is enhanced if it is kept in mind that it was a development from cumbersome verbal statements of quantitative relationships to brief and simple symbolic notations of the same relationships. Once particular symbolic notations have gained general scientific acceptance (and it will be seen that this is often a matter of centuries), they become most valuable tools which can then be used in further and more complex constructions.

Various algebraic concepts and operations are treated, either substantially or incidentally, in other chapters of this volume. In this chapter, it is the notational symbols of algebra—its conceptual tools—which are mainly singled out for study. (Negative numbers and theory of equations are also considered.) Although current notational systems are now universally accepted, their history is one of protracted and significant intellectual struggle on the part of the scientists who devised and perfected them.

It may not be an exaggeration to say that the full scientific maturity of algebra has depended most of all upon the development of simple and easily manipulated symbols, which have evolved out of clumsy verbal statements of relatively little scientific utility. In teaching children, however, as is shown later, it is often helpful to deal first with the symbols in verbal form.

81

Dantzig defines algebra in its broad sense as that branch of mathematics which deals with operations upon symbolic forms. "In this capacity," he writes, "it not only permeates all of mathematics, but encroaches upon the domain of formal logic and even of metaphysics. Furthermore, when so construed, algebra is as old as man's faculty to deal with general propositions; as old as his ability to discriminate between *some* and *any*." [3]

In the 1952 edition of the *Encyclopaedia Britannica*, "algebra" is defined as "that branch of mathematics which considers primarily the representation of numbers by means of letters . . . more precisely, it is that part of mathematics which considers the relations and properties of numbers by the aid of general symbols, usually letters $(a, b, c, \ldots, x, y, z)$ and signs of operation $(+, -, \times, \ldots)$ and relation $(=, >, <)$." Algebraic symbolism and operations are described as part of almost all branches of science, including the various subdivisions of mathematics from the elementary through the most complex levels of each.

By contrast, note the definitions of "mathematics" and "algebra" that appeared in the very first edition of the *Encyclopaedia Britannica*, published in 1771:

> Mathematics, originally signified any discipline or learning; but at present, denotes that science which teaches, or contemplates whatever is capable of being numbered or measured, in so far as computable or measurable; and accordingly is subdivided into Arithmetic, which has numbers for its object and Geometry which treats of magnitude.

> Algebra is a general method of computation by certain signs and symbols, which have been contrived for this purpose, and found convenient. It is called an Universal Arithmetic, and proceeds by operations and rules similar to those common in arithmetic, founded upon the same principles. But as a number of symbols are admitted into this science, being necessary for giving it that extent and generality which is its great excellence, the import of those symbols must be clearly stated.

These passages capture the flavor of the time in mathematics. The description of algebra, in particular, suggests a rather empirical, tentatively burgeoning field—a notion which is not part of present-day definitions.

Nesselmann (1842) classified the development of algebra into three periods: the rhetorical, in which algebraic ideas were written out in words; the syncopated, which embraced abbreviated forms for frequently used words; and the symbolic, in which symbols unrelated to the operations they represent replaced abbreviations in much the same way they do today.[4] Although it can be said in general that algebra did pass through all three stages in each of its culture locales,[5] there were, as in most historical classifications, overlappings.

According to Smith, the history of algebra as it is known today begins in the seventeenth century; algebraic problems solved geometrically (essentially without the use of algebra) stem from the time of the Alexandrian School (c. 300 B.C.); and problems now considered algebraic were first solved by guessing or by some arithmetic method as early as 1800 B.C.[6]

Neither Nesselmann's nor Smith's classification need be taken to represent exact lines of demarcation; but both may be helpful to the student in the process of ordering information about the development of algebra as a branch of mathematics.

No plea is made here for including the history of algebra in school curriculum. One needs to be well grounded in algebraic theory in order to comprehend and appreciate the threads of development in this branch of mathematics. But with increasing emphasis on introducing certain algebraic ideas in elementary mathematics programs—including simple equations, signed numbers, and the use of letters to represent numerical quantities—some awareness of the beginnings of algebra and highlights in its progress as a science seem indicated, particularly as background material for teachers. This chapter offers such material—first in a rather wide-ranging history touching on a variety of ideas and symbols, then in more detailed accounts of the basic operational symbols and the sign of equality.

A SELECTIVE HISTORY

The Early Centuries

Early traces of algebraic ideas are found in clay tablets of the Sumerians, in ancient Egyptian papyri, in the writings of a few Hindu scholars, and in the works of the Chinese, the Arabs, and the Persians. And the Greeks solved many algebraic problems geometrically up through the time of Euclid.[7]

The Ahmes papyrus (Egyptian, c. 1650–1600 B.C.), one of the oldest mathematical manuscripts preserved (the original is in the British Museum), contains material on linear equations used to solve problems in distribution of food and other supplies.[8] In these equations the unknown is indicated by *hau*, meaning "heap," and the processes of addition and subtraction are shown by "the legs of a man walking towards the symbol of the operand or away from it."[9]

Diophantus, one of the most eminent of Greek mathematicians, is credited [10] with the first work (c. 250–275) in which algebraic symbolism has a significance comparable to the modern one and in which analytic methods were employed to solve equations. It was the custom of ancient writers outside of Greece to include in their treatises on mathematics a broad range of mathematics subjects. Diophantus wrote the first distinct work on algebra alone. *Arithmetica,* considered the most important of his three works, deals with the theory of numbers, as differentiated from computation, and includes topics such as first-degree and quadratic determinate equations (having a specific number of roots), which are presently part of the study of algebra. Smith says of Diophantus: "In general he anticipated by several centuries the progress of algebra as this progress appears in the works of other writers; and his work, while known to the Arabs, was not really appreciated until its discovery in Europe in the sixteenth century." [11]

The most distinguished Hindu mathematician of the seventh century, Brahmagupta, used algebra (c. 628) in solving astronomical problems. His works have substantial reference to negative numbers and to quadratic and first-degree simultaneous equations, as well as solutions to indeterminate equations.[12]

Historians differ in their views of the Hindus' role in algebraic development. Some scholars feel that the Hindus came very close to an algebraic symbolism used operationally, while others deny that they advanced beyond Diophantus. There is also uncertainty regarding how much of the Hindus' algebra was taken from the Greek.

Bell gives this account: "The Hindus of the seventh to the twelfth centuries A.D. had almost invented algebraic symbolism; the Moslems reverted in their classic age to an almost completely rhetorical algebra." [13] He cites Moslem algebra as having developed from the late Greek and from the Hindus. The Moslems acknowledged translating Hindu works but eventually they discarded any suggestion of operational symbols and wrote everything out in full—even the names for numbers: "The Moslem retrogression in this respect was as long a backward step as any in the history of mathematics." [14]

A most interesting feature of early Hindu algebra is mentioned by Bell: "The first skillful algebraists seemed to find indeterminate (diophantine) equations much easier than the determinate equations of elementary algebra. The reverse is the situation today." [15]

Of further interest is the fact that the Hindus were as competent in computation as the Greeks were in logical proof, and that neither had much interest in or proclivity for the strength of the other. Dantzig, noting the great achievements of the Greeks, asks:

> How is it that the nation which gave us geometry and carried this science so far, did not create even a rudimentary algebra? Is it not equally strange that algebra . . . also originated in India and at about the same time when positional numeration did? [16]

Perhaps it was the very concreteness of Greek mathematical thought, the almost singular interest in objects themselves, that accounts for that nation's lack of enthusiasm for algebra, an abstract science.

Lacking an extended number system—and, perhaps, an interest in logical proof—the Hindus themselves failed to develop a really scientific algebra. And so what we now call imaginary numbers (encountered in works of the ninth century) and negative numbers (twelfth century) were quickly cast aside as inexistent.[17] However, the Hindus are credited with certain contributions toward advances in operational symbolism. Among these are the use of letters to stand for unknown quantities, a suggestion of Āryabhatta in the sixth century; Brahmagupta's use of abbreviations for each of several unknowns, and for squares and square roots (seventh century); fractions written with numerator above and denominator below, as they are today, but without the bar; and a dot to indicate a negative number.[18]

Some of the names that have been given to algebra [19] were based on the idea that it was a way of getting at the true and hidden origins of things. One name having this meaning was *kigen seiho,* used by Kowa Seki (c. 1680). Mohammed ibn Mûsâ al-Khowârizmî of Baghdad and Damascus wrote the first work (c. 825) whose title contains the word "algebra." The Arabic form of the word was *al-jebr,* or *al-jabr,* from *al,* "the," and *jabara,* a verb meaning "to reset, rejoin, reconstitute." (In Spain, today, the word *algebrista* refers to a bone-setter.[20]) In the sixteenth century, Francois Vieta was to object to the name "algebra," suggesting the term "analysis." Smith believes that the use of the term "analysis" in modern advanced mathematics can be traced to Vieta's influence.

The title of the above-mentioned al-Khowârizmî work, which was based on Greek models, was *'ilm al-jabr wa'l muqabalah,* meaning the science of "restoration and opposition," or "reduction and cancellation." [21] This refers to what would now be called transposition and collection of terms in an equation.

These processes are thought to have been al-Khowârizmî's own idea. Otherwise his work, though impressive, was mainly a translation of Greek and Hindu material. Moreover, in an important sense it represents one of the backward steps to be found here and there in the history of mathematics. It was a reversion by its author to a purely rhetorical algebra (for reasons that seem not to be known)—whereas earlier Moslems had made some advances, following the Hindus, in symbolic notation. (Here is an example of his style: "What must be the amount of a square, which, when twenty-one dirhems are added to it, becomes equal to the equivalent of ten roots of that square?" That was his way of saying: $x^2 + 21 = 10x$.) Bell points out that two centuries later (c. 1010) the rhetorical tradition still flourished, used in al-Karkhî's *Fakhri*, known as an Arab masterpiece that includes quadratic equations approached geometrically. "If the facts were not well established," he adds, "it would be difficult to believe that medieval European algebraists had the persistence to find out what the rhetorical algebraists of Islam were attempting to communicate." [22]

By the middle of the twelfth century, Bhāskara (1114 – c. 1185), a Hindu mathematician of great renown, had written the *Bija Ganita* (meaning "seed counting" or "seed arithmetic"), which dealt with signed numbers. The Sanskrit word for "debt" or "loss" stood for a negative quantity and was symbolically shown not by a minus sign but by a dot over the numeral: $\overset{\bullet}{5}$. The idea of imaginary numbers was still far from being recognized. In Bhāskara's manuscript it is stated that a negative quantity does not have a square root because it is not a square. When more than one unknown quantity was involved, color names were used to designate them. Irrationals were treated extensively, although lack of adequate symbolism made this an exceedingly difficult task. [23]

The Arabs learned from both the Greeks and the Hindus and transmitted these learnings to Europe in the twelfth century when they settled in Spain. In fact, their major contribution to mathematics is frequently cited as that of preserving and handing down the work of classic Greek mathematicians. They did, however, demonstrate some originality in algebra and trigonometry. Among the most brilliant of Arab contributions to mathematics was that of Omar Khayyám, in the eleventh century. The poet of the *Rubáiyát* (written in Persian) can be thought of as the originator of graphical methods in mathematics; and in his Arabic algebra he used Greek geometry and Hindu algebra for the solutions to cubic and quartic equations. [24]

In the thirteenth century, a German mathematician, Jordanus Nemorarius, used letters to represent numbers in much the same way as they are used today. (This was done to a lesser extent in the works of Aristotle and Diophantus.) [25]

Advances in algebra were also made in China during the thirteenth century. [26] Ch'in Kiu-shao (c. 1247), a prominent scholar of this period, dealt with equations of an advanced nature and with the application of algebra to trigonometry, treating algebra as a pure science. Chu Shi-kie (late thirteenth century) dealt with rules for algebraic signs, provided an introduction to algebraic processes, dealt with problems of higher equations, and brought the abacus algebra to its highest point. In this last connection, coefficients were represented by sticks.

During the long span of centuries from the beginnings up through the fourteen hundreds, there were of course many other scholars—too many to mention—who made significant contributions to the growth of algebra. For the present purpose it seems well to summarize at this point the two most important facts about early algebra: (1) Although some symbolism was used in these early cultures, the algebra of the Egyptians, Babylonians, Greeks, Hindus, and Arabs was primarily rhetorical. (2) "The scope of all early algebra was limited to a study of equations or to the solution of problems which at present would be solved by their aid." [27]

The Sixteenth to Nineteenth Centuries

With the advent of printing in the sixteenth century, the field of algebra began to grow into a more generalized arithmetic through the work of such mathematicians as Rudolff and Recorde. But even then symbolism was still in a relatively crude state—still to be perfected in the seventeenth century, when it would contribute largely to a more rapid development of algebra and to the beginnings of algebra's contributions to the development of higher mathematics. Kline suggests that the invention of modern symbolism was the "consequence of the pressure on mathematicians to keep pace with the rapidly expanding and deepening use of mathematics during the rise of modern science." [28]

Cardan's *Ars Magna* (1545), written in Latin, was the first algebra of significance to be published—a work concerned primarily with solutions to algebraic equations. Two solutions, in particular, have historical interest. One is Ferrari's solution to a fourth-degree biquadratic equation, $x^4 - 6x^2 + 36 = 60x$. Cardan, unable to solve the problem, had given it to Ferrari, who was his student. Ferrari himself, a prominent Italian mathematician, died at the age of thirty-eight (c. 1560) in his first year of service as professor of mathematics at Bologna, leaving no writings on mathematics.[29]

The other solution is that of Tartaglia (1500–1557), who was among the greatest of sixteenth-century Italian mathematicians. Tartaglia had worked out a solution to the cubic equation and shared it with Cardan, pledging him to secrecy. The inclusion of Tartaglia's solution in *Ars Magna* was considered by some dishonorable on Cardan's part; another view was that withholding information which could contribute to cultural advancement was inexcusable and that Tartaglia had no right to demand secrecy.[30] Cajori, writing in the nineteenth century, cited the solution of cubic equations as the chief sixteenth-century contribution to algebra and lamented that Tartaglia, the man responsible for it, had been too often forgotten. "Cardan was a good mathematician," he acknowledged, but "the association of his name with the discovery of the solution of cubics is a gross historical error and a great injustice to the genius of Tartaglia." [31]

In the ranks of Cardan and Tartaglia were other prominent Italian mathematicians of the Renaissance period who contributed to the advancement of the science of algebra: Pacioli, in his *Suma* (1494), summarized what was known about the subject up to that date; Rudolff, in *Coss* (1525), invented improved symbols for radicals; Bombelli, recognized for his work on solutions of cubic and biquadratic equations, prepared the first textbook with the word *algebra* in the title (1572), a work which was particularly systematic and one in which the teaching of algebra was considered.[32]

By 1572, the content of elementary algebra was pretty well established, but the development of an adequate symbolism was yet to be completed. Among those largely responsible for this accomplishment were Vieta (c. 1590), Harriot (c. 1610), Oughtred (c. 1628), and Descartes (1637).

Francois Vieta (1540–1603), a lawyer and perhaps the most eminent sixteenth-century French mathematician, introduced the idea of using a capital letter to represent a whole class of numbers; for example, letting X or Y stand for any even number.[33] John Wallis (1616–1703) infers that Vieta followed a legal custom of selecting an arbitrary name to designate a case, a custom which led to using only the initials and eventually just a single capital letter (A, B, C, etc.). As has already been mentioned, early mathematicians such as Diophantus had used letters as symbols for unknown quantities—but these instances had involved a particular unknown number, not a whole class of numbers. Vieta differentiated these two ideas by referring to the former as "logistica numerosa" and the latter as "logistica speciosa." Still the notion of symbolism in mathematics grew slowly.

Harriot, a surveyor and astronomer, was responsible for a standard algebra textbook which has had general recognition since its publication in 1631 some time after his death. He used small consonants and vowels for known and unknown quantities respectively, $\sqrt{3}$ for the cube root, the sign $>$ for "greater than," and $<$ for "less than." These last two symbols, suggested by Harriot in 1631, eventually replaced $\sqsubset$ and $\sqsupset$, which were those of Oughtred, suggested in the same year and at the time favored by many writers.[34] Oughtred also introduced the modern multiplication sign, $\times$, and $::$ for proportion.[35]

Cajori gives the following examples of Vieta's and Harriot's use of symbols as compared with those in modern use: [36] In Vieta's notation, $x^3 + 3bx = 2c$ would be written A *cubus* + B *plano* 3 *in* A, *aequari* Z *solido* 2. And Harriot's notation for $x^3 - 3b^2x = 2c^3$ would be *aaa* − *3bba* = *2ccc*. He also illustrates from Oughtred's *Clavis Mathematicae* (1631) A^{10} appearing as *Aqqcc* and $120A^7E^3$ written as 120 *AqqcEc*.

The small letters q and c refer to the square and cube of an unknown quantity. Two q's are therefore equivalent to expressing the fourth power, two c's to expressing the sixth power.

Negative Numbers

Of major significance in the development of the science of algebra was the role of negative numbers. The early Hindus had recognized the value of negative numbers. They used them to express direction with respect to a reference point and to express assets and debts.[37] In Europe, however, strange as it may seem, it was not until the seventeenth century that the idea of negative quantities took root.

Cajori's account indicates that, although negative roots had emerged in various mathematical works prior to the seventeenth century, they were not considered important; the mathematicians confined their concerns to the positive quantities. Cardan recognized negative roots, but referred to them as "fictitious" and to positive roots as "real." [38] Stifel used the phrase "less than nothing" to denote negative numbers, and also the term "absurd numbers." "It took about 300 years," Cajori says, "to eliminate this senseless phrase ['less than nothing'] from mathematical language." Vieta, who was largely responsible for developing modern algebraic symbolism, knew only positive roots. It was Harriot who first placed a negative term by itself on one side of an equation.[39]

"The full interpretation and construction of negative quantities and the systematic use of them begins with René Descartes (1596–1650), but after him erroneous views respecting them appear again and again." [40] Carnot (1753–1823), a French mathematician noted for his work in geometry, thought negative numbers resulted in inaccurate conclusions. And in 1831, De Morgan, distinguished for his contribution to logic, felt that negative numbers as roots of an equation showed either error in the statement of the problem or that the problem had no solution.[41]

It was about one hundred years ago that mathematicians reached the point of being able to extend their concept of number to include negative and irrational terms. The former became useful to represent debts, the lattter to represent lengths—both physical uses of number.[42] And "not until the middle of the nineteenth century was the subject of negative numbers properly explained in school algebras." [43]

Cajori discusses the question of why it was so difficult to include the idea of the negative in the concept of number. Reasoning that until mathematicians "hit upon a visual or graphical representation of them," negative numbers seemed "absurd" or "fictitious," he comments on the importance of such representations in the teaching of algebra. "Omit all illustrations by lines, or by the thermometer," he warns, "and negative numbers will be as absurd to modern students as they were to the early algebraists." [44]

Theory of Equations

Analytic decomposition of equations, commonly referred to as "theory of equations," is a highly complex area of mathematical study. However, some elementary school programs have touched upon such structural patterns as they apply to simple equations, and for this reason a few brief developmental references are made here, all based on or quoting from Cajori's *History of Elementary Mathematics* (1896), pages 230–36.

Vieta was able to achieve some understanding of the relationship between the coefficients and roots of an equation, but his dealing exclusively with positive roots precluded broader perspective. Jacques Peletier (1517–1582) is credited with having noted that "the root of an equation is a divisor of the last term." Girard, a Flemish mathematician who was first to apply negative roots to geometric solutions (1629), "inferred by induction that every equation has as many roots as there are units in the number expressing its degree." And Descartes's "rule of signs," a theorem by which the number of positive and negative roots of an equation could be determined, was another significant contribution to the theory of equations. His wording was of particular importance, since the rule does not apply in instances of imaginary roots: "An equation *may* have as many positive roots as there are variations in sign, and as many negative roots as there are permanences in sign." For example, $5x^3 - 2x^2 - x + 4$ has two variations and one permanence. ("Permanence" refers to two consecutive like signs in a series of positive and negative terms.)

Girard was also first to recognize a pattern relating the sum and product of the roots of an equation, and his concept of number encompassed both imaginary and negative quantities. He noted that the sum of the roots of an equation yielded the coefficient of the second term with the sign changed, and that the product of the roots was the same as the coefficient of the third term. To illustrate with a simple equation, $x^2 + 2x - 15 = 0$, the roots of which are -5 and $+3$: The sum of the roots -5 and $+3$ is -2. This is the coefficient of the second term with the sign changed. The product of the roots is -15, the third term of the equation.

Harriot had found these same relationships between coefficients and roots at about the same time (in England), but his work was on the simplest level and did not include imaginary and negative roots. Therefore he missed coming to grips with a generalization for the structure of all equations.

Exponential Notation

Simon Stevin (1548–1620) of Belgium is named by Cajori as having devised an exponential notation which grew out of his notation for decimal fractions and eventually became a part of basic modern symbolism.[45] He originally used a circle to denote the unknown and a numeral placed inside the circle to show the exponent or power. For instance, ①, ②, ③ represented x, x^2, x^3. Fractional exponents were likewise indicated: $(\frac{1}{2}) = x^{1/2}$. Cajori also gives this example, in which M stands for multiplication, *sec* for second term, and *ter* for the third unknown: 3 ① M *sec* ① M *ter* ②. Transcribed into current algebraic symbolism, this expression reads: $3xyz^2$. Stevin's structural pattern for exponential notation has survived; his symbol for the unknown was replaced by letters of the alphabet by Descartes (1637), who introduced the last letters of the alphabet to stand for unknown quantities and the first letters for known quantities. There is, however, no evidence of negative or fractional exponents in Descartes's work. In this respect Stevin surpassed him.

Mathematicians of Stevin's and Descartes's era employed a variety of notational techniques. In fact, throughout the seventeenth century and into the eighteenth there was considerable diversity in exponential notation. The examples and appraisals to follow in this section are, with one exception, based on or quoted from Cajori's *History of Mathematical Notations* (1928), Volume I, pages 344–60.

A Swiss mathematician, Joost Bürgi, used Roman numerals for exponents,[46] writing $\overset{vi}{8}$ to stand for $8x^6$. As algebraic expressions became more complex, Roman numerals proved ineffective for exponential use. Moreover, Cajori's illustration of $\overset{ii}{15} - \overset{ii}{16}$ for the present $15x^2 - 16y^2$ shows clearly the need for including a symbol for the base to which an exponent (or a coefficient) refers. In Italy, Marini Ghetaldi (1630) placed coefficients in a subscript position: $m_2 + n$ stood for $2m + n$.

In 1636, James Hume introduced a superior notation, placing the exponent (expressed in Roman numerals) above the regular line and a little to the right of the base. That is, he wrote A^{iii} for A^3. "Thus, this Scotsman, residing in Paris, had almost hit upon the exponential symbolism which has become universal through the writings of Descartes."

Hume's $5a^{iv}$ was written by Hérigone as $5a4$ and by Descartes as $5a^4$. Printers understandably preferred Hérigone's notation, but that of

Descartes "offered certain advantages in interpretation which the judgment of subsequent centuries has sustained. Descartes used positive integral exponents only."

After the introduction of Cartesian exponential notation (1637), other notations were suggested from time to time, some as late as in the eighteenth century. None received general support and acceptance. A comparison of these with those of Descartes would "serve to indicate how the science might have been retarded in its progress under the handicap of cumbrous notations had such wise leadership as that of Descartes, Wallis, and Newton not been available."

The Cartesian exponential notation was adopted slowly among writers, with some mathematicians combining new symbolism with old until eventually the older systems became extinct.

The modern forms for negative and fractional exponential notation were devised by Wallis and Newton. Cajori's research shows that in 1676 Newton explained their use in a letter to the secretary of the Royal Society of London: "Since algebraists write a^2, a^3, a^4, etc., for aa, aaa, $aaaa$, etc., so I write $a^{1/2}$, $a^{3/2}$, $a^{5/3}$, for $\sqrt{a}$, $\sqrt{a^3}$, $\sqrt{ca^5}$; and I write a^{-1}, a^{-2}, a^{-3}, etc., for $1/a$, $1/aa$, $1/aaa$, etc."

In his concluding comments to a section on algebraic symbolism, Cajori notes the elasticity of Cartesian exponents, citing the ease with which it was possible to extend a^3 to general exponents, such as a^n, and the readily accomplished introduction of negative and fractional exponents which, in turn, paved the way for Euler (1740) to experiment with exponents for pure imaginary or complex numbers. From that point on, interpretations were possible that led to certain general theories. "Our exponential notation," says Cajori, "has been an aid for the advancement of the science of algebra to a degree that could not have been possible under the old German or other early notations. Nowhere is the importance of good notation for the rapid advancement of science exhibited more forcibly than in the exponential symbolism of algebra."

SYMBOLS FOR OPERATIONS AND EQUALITY

The course of development of the arithmetic operational symbols, $+$, $-$, $\times$, $\div$, provides an interesting record of part of man's efforts toward achieving a perfected notational system.

One might reasonably expect that the operational symbols of arithmetic preceded the development of algebraic symbolism. This surprisingly is not the case. According to Smith, these elementary arithmetic symbols "are almost wholly algebraic, most of them being transferred to the numerical field only in the 19th century," partly as an aid to

printers and partly because the educational system of that time required a written analysis for problems.[47] Arithmetic symbols are con-
spicuously absent from almost all of the textbooks of the seventeenth
and eighteenth centuries. Recorde, responsible for the modern equals
sign, used it only in his algebra, the *Whetstone of Witte* (1557), although he also published an arithmetic book. Smith mentions that
Hodder gives no symbols in his 1672 text (the first English arithmetic
reprinted in the American colonies, Boston, 1719) before page 201,
where he says: "Note that a + thus, doth signifie Addition, and two
lines thus ⊒ Equality, or Equation, but a × thus, Multiplication."
These were the only symbols Hodder used.[48]

Early writers devised various methods to signify addition, subtraction, multiplication, and division, often simply using words or abbreviated forms of words. This practice extended into later centuries and
can be observed in the notation of Stevin, where *M* is the symbol for
multiplication. (See page 91.)

The material to follow in this section focuses on a few paramount
features in the origin and development of the symbols themselves, as
distinguished from words (the Romans used the phrase *plus aut minus*
to mean "more or less"),[49] and the references are limited to their operational meanings.

Addition and Subtraction

The plus and minus signs as known today came into use in Germany
in the late fifteenth century. The material presented here on their
origins is, where not otherwise indicated, based on Cajori's *History of
Mathematical Notations* (Volume I, pages 230–45).

The symbol for addition, +, is thought to have evolved from the
use of the word *et* as found in fifteenth- and sixteenth-century Latin
manuscripts; for example, 5 *et* 3 denoted the addition process.[50] Its
resemblance to the plus sign, especially when written rapidly, strongly
suggests that this was the origin of the modern symbol.

The minus sign, referred to as *minnes*, first appeared in a 1481
German algebra manuscript (Dresden Library, C. 80), with the sign
occasionally being placed after the numeral to be subtracted.

A Latin manuscript of the same collection shows both the plus and
minus signs as operational symbols, with the plus sign occasionally used
to mean "and." The word *et*, however, is consistently used to indicate
addition.

These two symbols first appeared in print in J. Widman's arithmetic
of 1489. According to Cajori, Widman had studied the above-mentioned manuscripts and was very likely influenced by the symbolic
representations he found in them. Although Widman used the plus

and minus signs in the algebraic sense, his work also shows the signs used as other than operational symbols: the plus to mean "and," the minus to indicate the separation of two terms or values.

Examination of the problems presented in Widman's book resulted in differing opinions regarding the original significance of the plus and minus signs. One view, held by both De Morgan and Gerhardt, was that the two symbols stemmed from warehouse marks noting weight excess or deficiency. Regarding the minus sign, one view [51] of some credibility is that originally this operation was shown by the use of the word "minus" (as early as 1202 in Fibonacci's work), later by the letter m superscribed as $\widetilde{m}$ or $\overline{m}$, and eventually by the superscript alone.

During the late fifteenth century, Italian mathematicians adopted $\overline{p}$ and $\overline{m}$ as abbreviations for "plus" and "minus," and these forms competed with the symbols $+$ and $-$ into the early seventeenth century before the traditional symbols won their established place in mathematics notation.

That any other subtraction sign could have been suggested and used for several centuries by prominent writers is indeed curious in view of the particular simplicity and appropriateness of the traditional symbol, which had already achieved wide acceptance. Nevertheless, the sign recognized today as a division symbol, $\div$, was for four hundred years used to denote subtraction by many German, Swiss, and Dutch writers. The sign is still occasionally found for subtraction in twentieth-century books of Scandinavian countries. One possible explanation for its persistence is that it was intended to eliminate confusion, since the traditional symbol was used not only to indicate subtraction, but also as a dash, and to separate terms in a proportion. Cajori's research credits some mathematics historians with recognizing that writers of past centuries used the symbol $\div$ for "minus," but "none of the historians revealed even a suspicion that this symbol had an almost continuous history extending over four centuries."

Still other symbols for subtraction are found in sixteenth- and seventeenth-century writings: successive dashes, for example, or two or three dots, as used by Descartes in his *Géométrie*. In these centuries the lack of standardization often resulted in several different symbols for subtraction appearing on the same page in a given book or manuscript. The signs $-$ and $\div$, however, were the most common.

It was the Swiss mathematician J. H. Rahn who, finding two signs for subtraction ($-$ and $\div$) but none for division, remedied this state of affairs by assigning the $\div$ to represent division. His own countrymen expressed no interest in adopting this practice, but in England the proposal was enthusiastically received and implemented.

The story of the subtraction symbol is but one example of the diffi-culties encountered in achieving a common world-language of mathe-matics. As Cajori has observed:

> Centuries slip past before any marked step toward uniformity is made.
> It appears, indeed, as if blind chance were an uncertain guide to lead
> us away from the Babel of languages. The only hope for rapid approach
> to uniformity in mathematical symbolism lies in international co-opera-
> tion through representative committees.

Multiplication

Multiplication symbols developed considerably later than those of addition and subtraction, possibly because they served no early prac-tical use such as that of the marks + and − to indicate whether a sack or barrel exceeded or fell short of a required amount. The brief account given here of signs for multiplication is based mainly on Cajori's *History of Mathematical Notations* (Volume I, pages 250–68).

An old, mutilated Hindu manuscript probably written in the eighth, ninth, or tenth century was unearthed in 1881 in a small village of India. It is called the Bakhshālī manuscript [52] and has signs (either words or symbols) to indicate the operations of addition, subtraction, and division. Multiplication, however, was shown by placing numerals side by side without a sign, except in the case of fractions, where, for example, 4 1/2 meant 4 + 1/2, not 4 × 1/2. Perhaps this practice was a precursor to the modern algebraic one of having no sign between letters to signify multiplication. "In medieval manuscripts and early printed books," according to Cajori, "X was used as a mathematical sign, or a combination of signs, in eleven or more different ways," but he adds that his research "failed to bring to light a clear and con-clusive case where before Oughtred X was used as a symbol for mul-tiplication." The St. Andrew's cross as a multiplication sign came into use about 1600 in England: a large one (X) was used by Edward Wright, a smaller one (×) by Oughtred. Probably this modern symbol stems from instances of cross multiplication that were common to both arith-metic and algebra. During the seventeenth and eighteenth centuries, other signs designating multiplication included the rectangle used by Hérigone, the Hebrew letter ⊃ (*mem*) employed by Jones, Rahn's six-pointed star, and the comma used by Van Schooten and others. Not until the nineteenth century did the modern sign take its place in ele-mentary arithmetic. Prior to that, Smith found, arithmeticians had no practical use for it.[53] Cajori reports that in 1698 Leibniz wrote in a letter: "I do not like × as a symbol for multiplication, as it is easily confounded with x; . . . often I simply relate two quantities by an interposed dot and indicate multiplication by $ZC \cdot LM$." Although the dot had appeared before Leibniz used it—in the twelfth-century manuscripts of Bhāskara [54] and in works by Harriot (1631) and Gibson (1655)—no clear explanation of its meaning was given; Leibniz is credited with having introduced this alternate symbol for multiplication.

Division

Early cultures had different ways of indicating that a quantity was to be separated into equal size parts. Here again, the historical account is based on Cajori's *History of Mathematical Notations* (Volume I, pages 269–75).

Diophantus used words to indicate division. An old Hindu manuscript shows division by the abbreviation *bha* from *bhaga*, meaning "part." The Hindus also wrote numbers one over the other to signify division or a fraction. Cajori believes that the fractional line was first referred to by an Arabic author, al-Hassâr, of the twelfth century. Al-Hassâr's example

$$\frac{3}{5}\ \frac{1}{3}$$

stood for "three fifths and one third of a fifth." An example of Leonardo of Pisa (who might possibly have antedated al-Hassâr in speaking of the fractional line),

$$\frac{1}{2}\ \frac{5}{6}\ \frac{7}{10}\ ,$$

meant seven-tenths, and five-sixths of one-tenth, and one-half of one-sixth of one-tenth.

In a passage from Leonardo's *Liber abbaci* (1202), here translated by Cajori, the fractional line is explained as follows:

> When above any number a line is drawn, and above that is written any other number, the superior number stands for the part or parts of the inferior number; the inferior is called the denominator, the superior the numerator. Thus, if above the two a line is drawn, and above that unity is written, this unity stands for one part of two parts of an integer, i.e., for a half, thus $\frac{1}{2}$.

Lunar symbols for division, 3)24 or 3)24(, are found in Stifel's work (1544) as well as in Oughtred's. Also in Oughtred's work there appears

$$\frac{4}{3}\Big]\frac{3}{2}\Big[\frac{9}{8}\quad\text{for}\quad\frac{3}{2}\div\frac{4}{3}=\frac{9}{8}\,.$$

Moxon's $D)A+B-C$ indicated the present $(A+B-C)\div D$. Other forms that have been employed include the letter D, sometimes in-

inverted, ⊓, or in lower case in horizontal position, ᴚ (DaCunha, 1790). Stevin wrote $(5x^2/y) \cdot z^2$ as follows: 5②D sec ①M ter ②.

The symbol ÷ for division, previously used by many writers as a minus sign, was introduced by Johann Rahn of Switzerland in his algebra of 1659. Praised by Leibniz and accepted in England and eventually the United States, the sign was not adopted by Swiss writers or in others parts of the European continent.

In 1668, Leibniz suggested using the letter C horizontally placed, ᴐ, for a division sign; but he later gave this idea up in favor of the colon (:), which he introduced in his *Acta eruditorium* (1684) for the first time: "Notetur, me divisionem hic designare hoc modo: x:y, quod idem est ac x divis, per y seu $\frac{x}{y}$."

Christian Wolf helped to influence the adoption of the colon and dot for division and multiplication respectively in both Germany and France.

The colon has been used for division and ratio in Continental Europe and in most Latin American countries. One Latin American writer in 1878 used the sign ÷, another (1844) wrote division problems thus:

$$\left(\frac{6}{7} \backslash 3\right) = \frac{6:3}{7} = \frac{2}{7} \text{ and } 12\backslash3 = 4.$$

Three of the four operational signs eventually attained universal acceptance, thus moving toward a world-language of mathematics; the division symbols ÷ and : constitute the exception. With regard to these symbols, Cajori cites a National Committee on Mathematical Requirements recommendation of 1923:

> Since neither ÷ nor :, as signs of division plays any part in business life, it seems proper to consider only the needs of Algebra, and to make more use of the fractional form and (where the meaning is clear) of the symbol /, and to drop the symbol ÷ in writing algebraic expressions.

In the United States the colon has retained a place as a sign of proportion. During the nineteenth century the notation : :: : was in general use to indicate proportion; by the twentieth century the familiar form : = : was adopted.

Equality

One criticism of most mathematical symbols that have become traditional is that they do not in themselves suggest what they represent. An interesting exception is the equals sign, introduced by Robert Recorde (1557), an English mathematician who felt that parallel lines were more alike than anything he could think of: "I will sette as I doe often in woorke, vse, a paire of paralleles or Gemowe lines of one lengthe, thus: ————— , because noe .2. thynges, can be moare equalle." [55] This symbol for equality was slow to be adopted although in smaller form it eventually achieved universality. Rahn, in his algebra of a century later, felt it was necessary to explain its meaning because it might not be known to mathematicians.[56]

For some sixty years after Recorde's introduction of the equals sign it did not appear as such in published works. During this time the symbol was used to mean different things by different writers: [57] by Vieta (1591) to designate subtraction or arithmetic differences; by Descartes (1638) to signify the present $\pm$ (plus or minus); by Caramuel to indicate a decimal point. In this last instance $102=857$ represented the current 102.857. But, very interestingly, among the earliest equality symbols, there is in the Ahmes papyrus a sign closely resembling the modern one. Other mathematicians of the early centuries employed various means of signifying equality, such as a dash, a word, or a blank space. In printed books before Recorde, however, and in the works of many noted mathematicians before his time and a century later, no symbol for equality appears. It was most often expressed rhetorically by words like *aequales, aequantur, esgale, faciunt, ghelijck, gleich,* or the abbreviation *aeq.*

Other symbols appearing in significant works of several mathematicians competed with the equals sign for permanency in mathematical notation.[58] Among these were the bracket, [; parallel lines in vertical position, ||; a single vertical line, as in $A|B$ for $A=B$; the complex ⧓, suggested by two English writers who were father and son; and Hérigone's (1634) unusual 2|2. (His $a2+ba\,2|2\,b2$ is equivalent to today's $a^2+ab=b^2$.) For "greater than" and "less than" he used 3|2 and 2|3 respectively in a similar way. Hérigone sometimes used $\sqcup$ to express equality; and Leibniz used this sign inverted, $\sqcap$, for that purpose in unpublished works, as well as both the modern sign and the Cartesian (1637) identity symbol ∞. Leibniz's published works, however, have only the modern symbol.

Cajori indicates that the Cartesian sign for equality was the only real threat to that of Recorde. Descartes's *Géométrie,* recognized as a major mathematical contribution, was probably largely responsible for the adoption of his equality sign by a number of influential mathematicians of the seventeenth century.[59] It was particularly popular in France and Holland through the early eighteenth century. In England both Descartes's and Recorde's symbols were in use until the seventeen hundreds. Adopted first by Harriot and Oughtred and later by Wallis and Isaac Newton, Recorde's sign of equality prevailed.

Although Recorde's symbol was used by many prominent mathematicians during the seventeenth century, most writers of this period, according to Cajori, used Descartes's equality sign or none at all. Marking the beginning of the eighteenth century as the time when competition among symbols of equality ceased and Recorde's notation gained rapidly, Cajori sees Leibniz's preference for = over ∞ as being the influencing factor.[60]

IMPLICATIONS FOR EDUCATION

The foregoing material has been presented to show that algebra as a science developed very slowly over many centuries through the efforts of many people and cultures, and that although it has taken more than five thousand years for mathematics notation to reach its present level of development, the vast majority of the changes that led to that high level took place in a period of less than two hundred years—in the sixteenth and seventeenth centuries.

The key ideas in algebra which have become part of elementary education programs are ideas which also serve as necessary preparation for advanced study and thus constitute significant elements of the field.

Some notions related to algebraic development might easily be spelled out in a most enlightening fashion for children. A few suggestions are offered here.

Rhetorical algebra is still in use, as, for example, when the commutative law for addition is stated: The order of the addends produces no change in the sum. This mathematical principle can, of course, be phrased in a variety of ways, and children who have grasped the basic concept are likely to express it in their own less formal wording. An invitation to consider ways of stating such an algebraic principle as succinctly as possible could easily transmit to young people some idea of the developmental phases of algebra. It would then not be difficult to see how the frequently used statements of earlier times led to abbreviated forms and ultimately to more functional symbols. This simple but meaningful aspect of algebra is rarely, if ever, mentioned in mathematics curriculum materials.

At a more advanced level, children discovering that the product of the sum and difference of two numbers is the difference between their squares would appreciate the symbolism for this principle, $(a+b)(a-b)=a^2-b^2$, after attempting to represent it more compactly than as stated above.

Once young people recognize that algebraic symbols are used to stand for ideas that can always be expressed in words, they have a firm foundation for further study. But an idea expressed in words must first be carefully explored by students until its meaning is clear. Here Bertrand Russell recalls his own experience as a student:

> The beginnings of Algebra I found far more difficult [than geometry], perhaps as a result of bad teaching. I was made to learn by heart: "The square of the sum of two numbers is equal to the sum of their squares increased by twice their product." I had not the vaguest idea what this meant, and when I could not remember the words, my tutor threw the book at my head, which did not stimulate my intellect in any way.[61]

It is not unusual to find required memorization of rules in today's classrooms, although hopefully the trend is away from this procedure. And, too often, little or no emphasis is placed on interpreting the meaning of mathematical principles. In the problem just referred to, for example, if 3 and 5 are chosen as two numbers to represent a and b in the general algebraic statement, the symbolism and substitution would be as follows:

$$(a+b)^2 = a^2 + b^2 + 2ab$$
$$(3+5)^2 = (3)^2 + (5)^2 + 2(3 \times 5)$$
$$8^2 = 9 + 25 + 30$$
$$64 = 64$$

Analyzed another way, the problem might look like this:

The square of the sum of two numbers	$(3+5)^2$
is equal to the sum of their squares	$=9+25$
increased by twice their product.	$+2(3 \times 5)$

Students need directed opportunity to analyze mathematical concepts expressed in words and to recognize symbolic notation as a translation into the language of mathematics. Opportunity should also be provided for students to try many number combinations in mathematical statements to determine for themselves whether a generalization is justified or not.

The examples noted above are generalizations of particular numerical patterns expressed algebraically. Students who have been helped to look for patterns in mathematical structure and to arrive at consequent generalizations (see pages 123–24 for an illustration) should be well prepared to deal with the more abstract problems discussed here.

Things now taken for granted have often been a struggle for men of earlier times. The emergence and long-time rejection of negative roots is one notable example. Of lesser importance but of particular interest is De Morgan's report of Wallis's conflict regarding two equivalent notations:

Perhaps no man of his day had so much power over mathematical language as Wallis. But the following extract of a letter from him to Collins (Macclesfield Collection, vol. ii, p. 579), in 1673, shews that he once had doubts whether he might dare write down the square root of 12 as being twice the square root of 3, however certain he might be that it is so; because no one had so written it. Speaking of the square root of a negative quantity, he says, "Only, though I had from the first a good mind to it, I durst not without a precedent, when I was so young an algebraist as in the history my late letter reports, take upon me to introduce a new way of notation which I did not know of any to have used before." [62]

In the same vein, the importance of appropriate terminology can be interestingly demonstrated by having students attempt to express x^2, x^3, x^4, x^5, x^6 in words, assuming that the symbols have not yet been invented. The need for a term to express the square of the unknown (before x^2 was invented) resulted in the Greek "tetragon" number (literally, a four-sided figure). Diophantus's terms for the third, fourth, fifth, and sixth powers, respectively, were cube, power-power, power-cube, and cube-cube. He thus employed the additive rather than the multiplicative principle. [63]

Acquainting students with such historical anecdotes provides an opportunity for them to identify with the human role and conflict in the development of mathematics.

The usefulness of stating quantitative relationships algebraically has long been substantiated; and practical illustrations can often communicate this idea to students more forcefully than just the statement of facts.

An examination of the word problems in elementary algebra textbooks, however, often reveals little, if any, connection between the subject and the student's real world. Trivial word problems relating to age, coins, mixtures, and distances, familiar to this writer thirty years ago as a junior high school student, are still an integral part of programs in this present era when relevancy in the curriculum should have high priority.

It is of interest to note the comparable level of application of simple algebraic processes in typical problems of earlier cultures. The following two examples are quoted by Smith: [64]

1. Find a square from which if 15¾ is subtracted the result is its own root.

2. A man takes a passage in a ship and asks the master what he has to pay. The master says that it will not be any more than for the others. The passenger on again asking how much it would be, the master replies: "It will be the number of pesos which, when multi-

plied by itself and added to the number gives 1260." Required to know how much the master asked.

An example appearing in Bhāskara's *Lilawati,* a treatise on general theology of the eighth century, is given by Dantzig: [65]

A necklace was broken during an amorous struggle. One-third of the pearls fell to the ground, one-fifth stayed on the couch, one-sixth was found by the girl, and one-tenth recovered by her lover; six pearls remained on the string. Say of how many pearls the necklace was composed.

These puzzle-type examples are not unsimilar to those in current books. At least the human problem in the *Lilawati* example is real!

One wonders why algebraic illustrations are so often unrelated to real problems. Some clue to answering this question may be found in Kline's description of algebra as a collection of machines with mechanisms to convert complicated expressions into simpler forms which lead to problem solutions: "Elementary algebra as a whole is a huge machine to mechanize thinking. Like the complex machines of modern factories, it enables us to work wonders in almost no time." [66]

One example of algebraic machinery is factoring, a process which involves finding the expressions which were multiplied by each other to form a more complex collection of terms. For example, $(x-4)$ multiplied by $(x+6)$ yields the product $x^2+2x-24$. Therefore, the first two expressions are the factors of the third.

Kline acknowledges that in emphasizing the mechanization of algebra, "we are also stating that in itself elementary algebra is of no great interest. . . . In itself it has little to say; it serves a subsidiary purpose." [67]

Kline also likens the techniques of algebra to single notes in a musical masterpiece. When employed with understanding in a significant undertaking, they "form beautiful patterns of reasoning." But as separate processes, he says, they ought not to be thought of as mathematics.[68]

All this notwithstanding, of the many materials this writer has examined, Kline's alone have presented illustrations which can be classified as having various degrees of realistic application. The three examples that follow are drawn essentially from his *Mathematics and the Physical World,* pages 56, 61–62, and 63–65.

First is the instance of the young Gauss's almost immediate response when his teacher assigned the class to find the sum of the first one hundred whole numbers—in itself a dull task. The teacher had expected to have a block of free time in which to complete clerical details while the students worked on this problem. Gauss quickly observed that $1+100=101$; $2+99=101$; $3+98=101$; and so on. That is, he saw that there were 50 pairs of numbers each equal to 101. Therefore, 50 multiplied by 101 would give 5050, the sum requested. His knowledge and understanding of a particular mathematical pattern enabled him to solve the problem in a few moments rather than in the hour or more it would have taken to do it arithmetically. He was applying the formula

$$S=\frac{n}{2}(a+b)$$

for arithmetic progressions, in which S stands for the sum desired, n for the number of terms in the progression, a for the first term, and b for the last term. Substitution yielded:

$$S=\frac{100}{2}(1+100)=50(101)=5050.$$

Applying this formula to progressions with fewer terms allows one to grasp more fully the idea it represents. Note the following illustrations:

$$S=\frac{10}{2}(1+10)=5(11)=55 \qquad S=\frac{6}{2}(5+10)=3(15)=45$$

The second example, a classic story in the history of mathematics, is about the King of Syracuse (a city-state of ancient Sicily), who suspected that his new crown was not made of pure gold, as he had ordered, but partly of silver. He asked Archimedes, the greatest of ancient mathematicians, to determine whether he had been cheated, without destroying the crown.

In pondering the question, Archimedes connected an ordinary observation with a sound solution. He noted, as he got into his bath when the tub was full, that the amount of water that overflowed was equal to the amount by which his body was immersed. (The story goes that he was so excited by the clue this gave him that he ran out naked shouting "Eureka!") He knew that bodies of equal weight did not necessarily occupy the same volume and that, in particular, a pound of silver would displace more water than a pound of gold. Through experimentation with equally weighted mounds of pure silver and pure gold, and the crown itself, he learned that the crown was a mixture of silver and gold. Algebraic equations enabled him to find the exact amounts of each.

The third problem concerns the known fact that sound travels about

1100 feet per second in the air and about ten times as fast through solids. The Indians used to put an ear to the ground to determine whether a rider on horseback was approaching from a distance, and this is probably the origin of sayings about "keeping one's ear to the ground." The Indians, however, did not have algebraic symbolism and reasoning which make it possible to figure the distance of the source of a particular sound when it is heard first through the ground and then, say, 5 seconds later through the air. If $x/1100$ represents the time required for sound to reach the listener through the air, then $x/11000$ will stand for the time it takes to be heard through the ground, since it is 10 times faster. The equation

$$\frac{x}{1100} - \frac{x}{11000} = 5$$

shows the difference in time it takes the sound to reach the listener in 5 seconds. The value of x, when the equation is solved to the nearest whole number, is 6111, which means that the source of the sound is that many feet away.

The first of these three illustrations is based primarily on pattern and structure in the modern numerational system; the second and third examples connect the use of algebra with aspects of the physical world. Kline considers this latter case (approaching mathematics through its relationships with authentic physical problems) of major significance in mathematics education; and his works provide a valuable source of material concerning such relationships.

EIGHT

Structure

SYSTEMATIC IDEAS

The current concern with structure in the various disciplines has led to a particular emphasis on certain basic arithmetic principles—the laws of commutation, association, and distribution. Until the recent curriculum reform movement, these principles were usually first introduced at the college level.

Actually, students have always employed these concepts in their arithmetic work, but the ideas themselves were not treated as the generalizations they represent.

The five *basic laws* set forth the essential properties of addition and multiplication, the two primary operations on numbers. (They are stated on pages 111–12, following a discussion of generalized concepts of numbers and operations.)

That $3+5=5+3$ seems so obvious that one tends to accept it without question. It is, however, an example of the commutative law for addition in operation—one of the pillars of the arithmetic system.

Although these laws had been recognized by mathematicians who were involved with developing the symbolism for calculus, it was not until the beginning of the nineteenth century that they came into their own in the sense they are known today.[1] It was shortly after 1800, Bell says, that leading mathematicians undertook an "intensive scrutiny of mathematics itself." And he adds:

> Much of the resulting new mathematics made possible successful attacks on physical problems of the 19th and 20th centuries. The theory of matrices, for example, begun in 1858 by Arthur Cayley for purely formal algebraic purposes proved useful in the quantum theory of 1925.[2]

Whereas every recently published textbook for teachers of elementary school mathematics deals rather fully with the commutative, associative, and distributive laws, generally speaking the texts on mathematics history have very little material on the developmental background of these concepts.

Both Cajori and Smith note that the terms "commutative" and "distributive" in the usual algebraic sense are credited to the French mathematician Servois (1814), and that the term "associative" is thought to be derived from its use by Sir William Hamilton.[3] Cajori notes, too, that the Scotsman "Duncan Farquharson Gregory (1813–1844) wrote a paper on the real nature of 'symbolic algebra' which brought out clearly the commutative and distributive laws."

Eves and Newsom trace the early formulation of algebraic structure to British mathematicians in the first half of the nineteenth century. It was at this time that the properties of the commutative, associative, and distributive laws were recognized as fundamental structures. Until then, algebra had been considered a symbolic representation of arithmetic, as it still is in many high schools and colleges.[4]

More than 2,000 years ago, Pythagoras gave the concept of number a central place in his philosophy. Its progress since then can best be traced through the technical researches of mathematicians. Only a few of the fundamental essentials that have developed are treated in this chapter, but these serve to illustrate the qualities of abstractness and generality that are part of modern axiomatic methods. That such methods could be useful in formulating *number* concepts, as well as geometric ideas, was recognized by scholars of the late nineteenth century as they became aware of the arbitrary character of *all* mathematical systems. Full development and use of axiomatic procedures are achievements of the twentieth century.

NUMBERS AND OPERATIONS

The basic laws always hold true for the arithmetic of cardinal numbers, which with their addition and multiplication tables constitute the first number system to which children are introduced. The laws would not be so important, however, if they did not also apply to all the familiar number systems that people use. A classification of these sets of numbers is presented here. It is meant to be both understandable in terms of a general reader's eperience with numbers and also consistent with correct mathematical definitions.

> The *cardinal numbers* consist of zero and the numbers used for counting (0, 1, 2, 3, . . .). The counting numbers are often called the *natural numbers;* they are equivalent to the positive integers.

The *integers* are sometimes called the *whole numbers* (. . . , −2, −1, 0, 1, 2, . . .). They include integers equivalent to *all* of the cardinal numbers *and* integers that are the negatives of all these.

The *rational numbers* are classified as all those that can be expressed as fractions (e.g., −2/1, −3/2, −1/1, −2/3, −1/2, −1/3, 0/1, 1/3, 1/2, 2/3, 1/1, 3/2, 2/1). They include fractions equivalent to *all* of the integers, *and* other fractions *not* equivalent to any integer, *and* fractions that are the reciprocals of all of these (except zero).

The *real numbers* comprise all those that can be expressed as infinite decimals. They include numbers equivalent to *all* of the rationals. Some of these—the infinite *repeating* decimals—are equivalent to the cardinals, the integers, and the fractions that can be expressed as *finite* decimals (e.g., 2.000 · · · := 2.0, or 2/1, or 2; 1.500 · · · = 1.5, or 3/2; .7500 · · · = .75 or 3/4); others are equivalent to the fractions whose decimal representations are *not* finite (.666 · · · = 2/3; .333 · · · = 1/3).* And the real numbers *also* include all of the "irrational" numbers that can be expressed as infinite *nonrepeating* decimals and *cannot* be expressed as fractions (e.g., √2 = 1.414 · · ·; π = 3.1415 · · ·). The real number system is said to consist of exactly those numbers corresponding to *all* the points on a line. It is the most comprehensive number system that is in general use by educated people today, even if they seldom knowingly use "irrational" numbers.

From this classification it can be seen that each system includes some numbers equivalent to numbers in the other systems, and that each less extensive system is equivalent, as a *whole,* to *part* of each of the more extensive systems. These *equivalent* numbers are not the *same* numbers, but they are often spoken of as if they were, because they work the same way in their different systems. For example, the real numbers are said to "include" the rational numbers, the rationals to "include" the integers, and so forth. For the same reason, the numerals that are standard symbols for numbers in one system are often used to stand for their equivalents (if any) in other systems. For example, the numeral 3 may represent the cardinal number 3, or the integer 3, or the rational number 3 (the fraction 3/1), or the real number 3 (the infinite decimal 2.999 · · ·, which is equal to 3.000 · · · and may also be written 3.0). And the number represented by .333 · · · may be written 1/3, and vice versa.

The commutative, associative, and distributive properties of addition and multiplication, as stated in the basic laws, hold true not only for the familiar numbers, but for *all* number systems (including "complex

---

* Stevin, a Dutch mathematician, is responsible for the first systematic treatment of decimals (c. 1590), but it wasn't until two centuries later that rational numbers expressed as decimals came into popular use.

numbers"). Indeed it is exactly these properties of two primary operations that hold *numbers* together in *systems*. That is why the basic laws are *basic*. (The laws are also applicable to sets of elements that are different from ordinary numbers, under operations that bear little resemblance to addition and multiplication; and from the specification or invention of these modern abstract algebra has developed.)

The mathematicians and educational specialists who have developed new mathematics programs consider it important that students learn about numbers and their operations in such a way that these may be clearly and securely understood as interrelated structures in a unified and coherent system. They believe the curriculum should be a logical and articulated sequence that successively defines number operations in different ways for different sets of numbers, but in ways that show what properties are consistent from set to set and how a general, integrated, abstract concept of number grows out of these structural relationships.

But there are differences, among theorists and teachers alike, with regard to how, and at what grade levels, operations and numbers should be defined. Greater differences seem to exist concerning subtraction and division than for addition and multiplication. A possible explanation for this is that the meanings of addition and multiplication for the cardinal numbers are as a rule generally apparent in their elementary concrete interpretations—and inherent in their tables. Subtraction and division are to be understood eventually as secondary, or inverse, operations, in the sense that they are derived from the primary operations—addition and multiplication—and are defined in terms of them. As such, their meanings are more abstract, and more systematic, than those expressed verbally or graphically in terms of "taking away" (or "going backwards") or "how many times contained."

Writing mainly about modern secondary programs (1957), Bruce Meserve emphasizes the importance of *defining* things in terms *of sets of elements:* [5]

> Even though you may be reluctant to adopt some of the symbolism . . . , it should be clear that the basic properties of numbers ought to be presented to the students either as arising from properties of sets of elements or as arising from definitions which have been formulated so that the properties in the mathematical systems will be consistent with those of sets of elements.

And he goes on to say:

> Even in the elementary school, mathematics should be recognized, at least by the teacher, as a formal discipline based upon defined relations using sets of symbols which may be interpreted for many situations.

It turns out to be useful to define *any* "operation" on *any* set of elements in such a way that it satisfies this condition: When it is applied to *any* two elements of the set, in either order (e.g., $2+3$, or $3+2$), it must always *result* in an element of the *same set*. And if any two such operations satisfy the five basic laws, then the set of elements operated on constitutes a *number system*, and the elements are *numbers*.

This definition is intuitively compatible in a general way with what most people understand a "system" to be: a set of things, together with rules describing (or "laws" governing) how the things work in relation to each other. Moreover, the specific type of structure represented by the key concept of "number system" has not only had revolutionary impact on the study of logic; it has also had important practical applications, particularly for the design of electronic computers.

In his book *The New Mathematics* (1958), Irving Adler presents an exploration of number systems that is thorough and comprehensive and was written to be understood and enjoyed by any interested person who has knowledge of high school algebra and geometry. Like other modern analyses, it describes, step by step, "the expansion of the number system, from natural numbers to integers to rational numbers to real numbers to complex numbers." This sequence of steps roughly parallels the historical stages in the development of the concept of number—a development that might well be called "operation bootstrap," as Adler explains: [6]

> The system of natural numbers (the whole numbers used for counting) has defects that limit its usefulness . . . mathematics has lifted itself by its own bootstraps, using the defective system of natural numbers to construct bigger and better number systems that eliminate the defects.

The reader will notice that there are no "laws" concerning subtraction or division among the five basic laws. And this can be explained in terms of the "defects" in certain number systems that have led to the definition or construction of others. In each case a new system has elements and operations equivalent to those of a previous system, and new elements as well.

Subtraction cannot be properly regarded as an operation on the set of cardinal numbers, because it is *not always possible* in that system (e.g., there is no such cardinal number, or positive integer, as $2-3$); and when it *is* possible, it may be regarded as the way to answer a question about addition ("$5-3$" means "$5=3+?$"[*]). But subtraction is

---

[*] This question in another form is the equation $x+3=5$, which has the solution $x=2$. But the equation $x+5=3$ has no solution in the cardinal number system. It *does* have a unique solution in each of the more extended systems.

always possible in the system of whole numbers when it is *defined as addition:* "2−3" means "2+(−3)," or −1, which is a whole number.

Division is not always possible in the system of whole numbers (e.g., there is no such whole number as 3÷2, or 3/2); and when it *is* possible, it may be regarded as the answer to a question about multiplication ("8÷2" means "8=2×?"). Division is never possible by zero, but otherwise it is *always possible with rational numbers* when it is *defined as multiplication:* "3÷2," or "3÷2/1," means "3×1/2," or 3/2, which is a rational number. And "2/3÷4/5" means "2/3×5/4."

Similarly, the extraction of roots is not always possible in the rational number system (e.g., there is no fraction equivalent to $\sqrt{2}$); but it is always possible in the system of real numbers, which includes all infinite nonrepeating decimals.

It has been acknowledged that numerals for numbers in one system may stand for their equivalents (if any) in other systems. It is important, however, to understand that this does *not* mean, for example, that "fractions can be added to whole numbers." The expression 3+2/3 may mean 3/1+2/3, or it may mean 3.000···+.666···, depending on the context in which it appears. Every sum or product of numbers is *a number;* and any *number system* containing it also contains *all* its terms and factors and *all* other numbers with which it is multiplied, added, or even indirectly equated. For example, if an irrational number is involved in processing any of a group of related expressions, then *all* the numbers in the context are real numbers, which include both rational and irrational numbers. This fact is guaranteed by the equivalences (the technical term is "isomorphisms") that in effect create *systems within systems.*

Fortunately (and not by accident!) these same equivalences make it always possible to add, multiply, and subtract any numbers *equivalent* to cardinals or integers *as if they were* cardinals or integers, and to perform all operations on fractions and decimal numbers by adding and multiplying integers. Moreover, the equivalences also guarantee the consistency of many different interpretations, or meanings, of number operations and expressions. For example, 3+2/3 is *equal* to the rational number represented by the following expressions, in which all the terms and factors are rational numbers:

$$\frac{1}{3}(9+2)=\frac{9}{3}+\frac{2}{3}=9 \text{ thirds}+2 \text{ thirds}=3 \text{ ones}+\frac{2}{3}\text{of one}=\frac{1}{3}\text{of } 11$$

And in a real-number context these same expressions (and any others equal to 11/3) may represent the equivalent infinite decimal 3.666···, in which case all the terms and factors are real numbers.

THE BASIC LAWS

In the following material, each of the basic laws is explained; specific arithmetic illustrations are given; the commonly used algebraic generalizations are shown; and in some instances comments pertinent to application are made.

Commutative Laws

Commutative law for addition. The order of the addends does not affect the sum.

AN ARITHMETIC ILLUSTRATION: $\qquad\qquad 4+3=3+4$

AN ALGEBRAIC REPRESENTATION,
IN WHICH THE LETTERS a AND b
STAND FOR ANY TWO NUMBERS
IN A NUMBER SYSTEM: $\qquad\qquad a+b=b+a$

Commutative law for multiplication. The order of the factors does not affect the product.

AN ARITHMETIC ILLLUSTRATION: $\qquad\qquad 2\times5=5\times2$

AN ALGEBRAIC REPRESENTATION: $\qquad\qquad ab=ba$

A moment's experimentation is all that is necessary to convince one that the commutative principle is not applicable to subtraction or division. For example, $4-3$ is not equal to $3-4$; and $8/2$ is not equal to $2/8$. But when they are defined in terms of addition and multiplication, those basic operations *remain* commutative. For example: $2-3=2+(-3)=(-3)+2$. And $2/3=2/1\times1/3=1/3\times2/1$.

Associative Laws

Associative law for addition. The grouping of the addends does not affect the sum.

AN ARITHMETIC ILLUSTRATION: $\qquad\qquad 3+(7+5)=(3+7)+5$

AN ALGEBRAIC REPRESENTATION,
IN WHICH a, b, AND c
STAND FOR ANY THREE NUMBERS
IN A NUMBER SYSTEM: $\qquad\qquad a+(b+c)=(a+b)+c$

Associative law for multiplication. The grouping of the factors does not affect the product.

AN ARITHMETIC ILLUSTRATION: $\qquad\qquad 2\times(3\times4)=(2\times3)\times4$

AN ALGEBRAIC REPRESENTATION: $\qquad\qquad a(bc)=(ab)c$

Note. The commutative and associative laws for addition and for multiplication may be applied to problems with any number of addends or factors. It should be kept in mind, however, that addition and multiplication can be performed on only *two numbers at a time*. For this reason, the expression $3+5+7$, for example, is meaningless unless it is specifically understood to mean *either* $(3+5)+7$ *or* $3+(5+7)$ *or* one of the *ten other* meaningful expressions, involving *addition only*, that can be formed by different orderings and parenthetical groupings of the three numbers 3, 5, and 7. By doing the various additions, it can be confirmed (easily) that all twelve of these expressions represent the same number: 15. By applying *both* the commutative and associative laws many times, to *two numbers at a time*, it can be shown (not as easily as might be supposed) that for *any* set of three numbers, all twelve meaningful expressions involving only their addition, for example $a+(b+c)$ and $b+(a+c)$, are equal—and, in general, that all such sums formed by any arrangement of the same numbers, no matter how many, are equal. And, this being the case, one is justified in leaving parentheses out of any such expression, indicating that it doesn't make any difference in what order the additions are done. Similarly, all expressions involving only multiplications of any given set of numbers are equal.

The Distributive Law

Multiplication is distributive over addition. In other words: The product of a given number and the sum of several numbers, can be found by *either* (A) multiplying the given number by the sum of the several numbers, *or* (B) multiplying the given number by each of the several numbers and adding the resulting products.

AN ARITHMETIC ILLUSTRATION: $5(3+4)=5(3)+5(4)$

    A: $5(3+4)=5(7)=35$

    B: $5(3)+5(4)=15+20=35$

AN ALGEBRAIC REPRESENTATION: $a(b+c)=ab+ac$

As Mueller points out, "the modern algorism of multiplication is substantially a reflection of this distributive law." [7] In other words:

    $\begin{array}{r} 234 \\ \times 5 \\ \hline \end{array}$ is a representation of $5(200+30+4)$.

Note 1. The law of multiplicative distribution may also be applied to problems with any number of addends, but must first be understood for expressions with only two addends, for reasons explained in the *Note* on the commutative and associative laws. The law as stated algebraically above represents the minimum number of operations involved in this type of problem: on the left side, two (one addition and one multiplication); on the right, three (two multiplications and one addition.) It may be extended as follows:

$$a(b+c+d)=ab+ac+ad;$$

and it may be generalized as stated in the verbal explanation above, and in the following algebraic representation:

$$a(b+c+\ldots+p+q)=ab+ac+\ldots+ap+aq$$

It may also be generalized to transform a product of sums into a sum of products (or vice versa). For example:

$$(a+b)(c+d)=(a+b)c+(a+b)d=ac+bc+ad+bd$$

Note 2. When the distributive law is applied to fractions of certain special forms, its algebraic statement looks like this:

$$\frac{1}{a}\left(\frac{b}{1}+\frac{c}{1}\right)=\left(\frac{1}{a}\cdot\frac{b}{1}\right)+\left(\frac{1}{a}\cdot\frac{c}{1}\right)$$

And this may be written as follows:

$$\frac{b+c}{a}=\frac{b}{a}+\frac{c}{a}$$

This second statement looks like something that might be called a "distributive law for division (of whole numbers) with respect to addition." It should *not* be called that, because division is not possible for *all* whole numbers. However, the statement does indeed hold true for all cases in which b and c are both "divisible" by a.

This *distributive property of division* is a useful fact in elementary arithmetic; and it may be stated verbally as follows: The quotient of the sum of several numbers divided by a given number can be found by *either* (A) adding the several numbers and dividing their sum by the given number *or* (B) dividing each of the several numbers by the given number and adding the resulting quotients.

An arithmetic illustration: $\dfrac{8+12}{4}=\dfrac{8}{4}+\dfrac{12}{4}$

A: $8+12=20$
$\quad 20 \div 4 = 5$

B: $8 \div 4 = 2$
$\quad 12 \div 4 = \underline{3}$
$\qquad\qquad\ \ 5$

A division problem such as $2\overline{)486}$ can be viewed, then, as $2\overline{)400+80+6}$; and indeed the dividend in any such case may be regrouped in any way that might facilitate solution or analysis of a problem.

OTHER PRINCIPLES AND CONSTRUCTS

In addition to the basic commutative, associative, and distributive laws, there are other elements of mathematical structure which have relevance for the school curriculum, either for the students directly or as background understandings for teachers. Certain aspects of a few of these have been selected for discussion here.

Principles of Equality

A number of ideas about equal quantities are among the most fundamental assumptions underlying algebraic structure. Among Euclid's axioms, for example, were these familiar statements: (1) *Things equal to the same thing are equal to each other.* (2) *If equals are added to (or subtracted from) equals, the results are equal.* The second of these can, of course, be generalized as follows: *The same operation formed on equals yields equal results.*

Such principles, in combination with certain important constructs such as *identity elements* (zero and one) and the *inverse* of a number (its negative or reciprocal) are often used (more often, perhaps, "understood") in explaining or establishing a great many other facts, both simple and complex, of arithmetic and algebra.°

The equality principles seem to offer an excellent opportunity to avoid an error too often made in teaching subtraction, and to introduce at least tentatively the notion of negative numbers, even if students are not ready for systematic instruction in the algebra of negatives. To tell children "You can't subtract a larger number from a smaller one" is clearly to misinform them. Using an example such as $23-8$, and exhibiting the three algorisms shown here, one may show that you *can* subtract 8 from 3: you get a negative number (-5).

$$
\begin{array}{ccc}
23 & 10+13 & 20 \ + \ 3 \\
-8 & -8 & - \ 8 \\
\hline
15 & 10+ \ 5 & 20+(-5)
\end{array}
$$

This actually involves knowledge of certain facts about negatives, and their behavior under the basic laws, with which some students may not yet be ready to deal. For example, it depends on understanding that $-(0+8)=-0-8$, and that $20+(-5)=20-5$. However, a simple

° For an excellent brief treatment of some of these, see Saunders MacLane, "Algebra," in *Insights into Modern Mathematics* (23rd Yearbook, NCTM, 1957), pp. 100-05.

partial "proof" may be offered by observing that $10+13=23$ and $20+3=23$, and therefore $10+13=20+3$ (according to the first equality principle above). So if 8 is subtracted from both of these regroupings of 23, the answers are equal (according to the second equality principle). Therefore $10+5=20+(-5)=15$.

Principles of Compensation

The principles of compensation for subtraction and division have many useful applications in elementary and intermediate mathematics,* and procedures involving them are treated in current materials as well as in conventional programs. The principles themselves, however, are not treated in the same fashion as are the basic (commutative, associative, and distributive) laws; that is, they are not identified as being structurally consistent—as being, in children's terms, happenings they can always depend on in arithmetic. With the current stress on introducing simple algebraic ideas to young children, these principles have a logical place in mathematics instruction.

The principle of compensation for subtraction: The same amount added to (or subtracted from) the minuend and subtrahend produces no change in the remainder.

AN ARITHMETIC ILLUSTRATION:

$$
\begin{array}{lll}
14 & \text{(minuend)} & 14+1=15 \quad\ \ 15 \\
-\ 9 & \text{(subtrahend)} & \ \ 9+1=10 \quad -10 \\
\hline
5 & \text{(remainder)} & \qquad\qquad\qquad\ \ 5
\end{array}
$$

ALGEBRAIC REPRESENTATIONS:

$$a-b=(a+x)-(b+x)$$
$$a-b=(a-x)-(b-x)$$

This principle is especially useful in problems such as the one illustrated. Children enjoy and profit from doing this type of algorism *before* learning the regrouping process for subtracting larger numerals from smaller ones. (The regrouping process is essentially the traditional "borrowing" technique, but is based on meaning rather than mechanics.) A more striking example is this problem:

$$
\begin{array}{r}
2321 \\
-1994 \\
\hline
\end{array}
$$

The person who recognizes that adding 6 to both minuend and subtrahend will result in

* See Mueller, *Arithmetic* (1956), pp. 98, 102-03, 114-15, 161.

$$\begin{array}{r} 2327 \\ -2000 \\ \hline \end{array}$$

can immediately *see* the solution, 327, without having to go through the usual step-by-step procedure. In general, adding or subtracting an amount that makes the new subtrahend a power of 10 (10, 100, 1000 . . .) or a power of 10 multiplied by a number less than 10 (20, 300, 4000 . . .) provides a most effective use of the compensation principle for subtraction.

The principle of compensation for division: If the dividend and the divisor are each multiplied (or divided) by the same number (not zero), the quotient remains unchanged.

ARITHMETIC EXAMPLES:

Given:	$18 \div 6 = 3$
Multiplying 18 and 6 by 2:	$36 \div 12 = 3$
Dividing 18 and 6 by 3:	$6 \div 2 = 3$

ALGEBRAIC REPRESENTATIONS:

$$\frac{ax}{bx} = \frac{a}{b} \qquad \frac{a/x}{b/x} = \frac{a}{b}$$

This principle has broad application to the solving of algebraic equations. Grasping its mathematical significance in the early school years is essential preparation for future work.

Zero and Negatives

The *identity element* for any mathematical operation is that element which, when applied to any element of the set to which it belongs, leaves that element unchanged.

In the system of whole numbers, *if zero is added to any number, the result is that same number to which it was added.* That is:

$$a + 0 = a$$

Zero, then, is the *identity element for addition* in the integers. A number that works this way is often called a "zero-element." *

In terms of a zero-element, the negative of a number may be defined and subtraction redefined (as addition!) for an extended number system including both positive and negative numbers. The *negative of any number* symbolized by the letter a is written $-a$ and is properly

---

* The "zero element" also has another interesting property, with important applications in algebra: the product of zero and any number is zero.

spoken of as "negative a." And $-a$ is defined simply as the number which, when added to a, gives zero:

$$a+(-a)=a-a=0$$

(Note that -5 is the negative of 5, and 5 is the negative of -5.)

In general, for any two numbers a and b, the expression $a-b$, formerly representing subtraction, is then defined to mean $a+(-b)$, or a plus the negative of b.

These other facts about the arithmetic of integers (and any other numbers that have negatives) follow from the basic laws and other defined properties:

$$-(-a)=a \qquad\qquad\qquad -(-5)=5$$
$$(-1)a=-a \qquad\qquad\qquad (-1)\times5=-5$$
$$a-b=-(b-a) \qquad\qquad 2-3=-(3-2)=-1$$
$$(-a)(-b)=ab \qquad\qquad\qquad (-2)\times(-3)=6$$
$$(-a)b=a(-b)=-(ab) \qquad (-2)\times3=2\times(-3)=-6$$

And:

$$-(a+b)=(-1)(a+b)=(-1)a+(-1)b=(-a)+(-b)=-a-b$$

Note that the distributive law operates at one point in this series. Notice also how these facts work in the following arithmetic example:

$$(14+1)-(9+1)=14+1-9-1=14-9+1-1=14-9+0=14-9$$

If this seems familiar, it may be because it's another way of looking at the example given above for the principle of compensation for subtraction!

Rationals and Reciprocals

The *identity element for multiplication,* in the system of whole numbers, is the number one. *The product of one and any number is equal to that number:*

$$1\cdot a=a$$

(A number that works this way is sometimes called a "one-element," or "unity element.")

In terms of the multiplicative identity element of a number system, the *reciprocal of a number* is defined (see pages 118–19); and division can then be defined for any system, such as the rational numbers, in which every number (except zero) has a reciprocal.

The *rational numbers* are all those that can be expressed as fractions—that is, in the form a/b where a and b are *whole numbers* and b is not zero. It is clear that there is an important equivalence relation between rational numbers and the division of whole numbers: the quotient $(a \div b)$ of two whole numbers a and b is, if it exists, equivalent to the rational number a/b (e.g., $4 \div 2$, or 2, is equivalent to $4/2$, or $2/1$). And the *division of fractions* can be so defined that it is *always possible* and *always consistent* with the *division of whole numbers*.

But first some basic facts about the rationals need to be stated.

Since there are infinitely many fractions that are equal to any given fraction (e.g., $3/1 = 6/2 = 9/3 = \ldots$), it is necessary to have a definition, or test, for the *equality* of any two fractions. This test is carried out by "cross-multiplication" of the whole-number parts, thus:

$$\frac{a}{b} = \frac{c}{d} \qquad \text{IF} \qquad ad = bc$$

The basic operations on fractions are also defined in terms of the basic operations on their whole-number parts. *Addition* may be defined as follows (and surely this is one of the many new concepts and techniques that are easier than the old!):

DEFINITION: $\dfrac{a}{b} + \dfrac{c}{d} = \dfrac{ad + bc}{bd}$

EXAMPLE: $\dfrac{1}{2} + \dfrac{3}{4} = \dfrac{(1 \times 4) + (2 \times 3)}{2 \times 4} = \dfrac{4 + 6}{8} = \dfrac{10}{8}$

And *multiplication* is as follows:

DEFINITION: $\dfrac{a}{b} \cdot \dfrac{c}{d} = \dfrac{ac}{bd}$ EXAMPLE: $\dfrac{1}{2} \times \dfrac{3}{4} = \dfrac{1 \times 3}{2 \times 4} = \dfrac{3}{8}$

The *multiplicative identity element* in the rational number system is of course $1/1$, or 1. And any fraction of the form x/x is clearly equal to $1/1$. Therefore the product of any such fraction and any other fraction is equal to the original fraction:

$$\frac{a}{b} \cdot \frac{x}{x} = \frac{ax}{bx} = \frac{a}{b}$$

For *almost* every rational number a/b there is another, b/a, called its *reciprocal*. For example: the reciprocal of 3 is $1/3$; that of $2/3$ is $3/2$; and so forth, and vice versa in each case. (The single exception is that zero has no reciprocal; there is no number of the form $a/0$.*) And what is important about reciprocals is this: *The product of any*

---

* If there were such a number as $3/0$, for example, it would be equivalent to a whole-number quotient $3 \div 0$, which would mean that some whole number times zero is equal to 3.

*number and its reciprocal is equal to the multiplicative identity
element* (the number one). Thus:

$$\frac{a}{b} \cdot \frac{b}{a} = \frac{ab}{ba} = \frac{1}{1} = 1$$

Now it is possible to define *division* as an operation on the rational
numbers.

First it should be noted that an expression such as A/B, where A
and B are themselves fractions, is commonly called a "complex *fraction.*" (Suppose $A = 1/2$ and $B = 3/4$, for example.) Moreover it looks like,
and is commonly called, a "*quotient* of fractions." What is needed, then,
is to define such expressions, in terms of the basic operations and properties of fractions, so that A/B is in fact always a rational number
(equal to some fraction a/b where a and b are whole numbers), *and*
so that the meaning of A/B is consistent with the meaning of whole-
number division.

All this is achieved if A/B (or $A \div B$) is defined to mean A *times the
reciprocal of B* .Thus, if $A = c/d$ and $B = f/g$:

$$A \div B = \frac{A}{B} = \frac{c/d}{f/g} = \frac{c}{d} \cdot \frac{g}{f} = \frac{cg}{df}$$

This definition guarantees that A/B is always a rational number, simply
because it is the product of two rationals. In other words, the definition
describes a simple, specific, and infallible method for renaming a
complex fraction as ("reducing" it to) a simple fraction. (It is commonly
called the "invert and multiply" method of dividing fractions.) For
example:

$$\frac{1/2}{3/4} = \frac{1}{2} \times \frac{4}{3} = \frac{4}{6}$$

Since $A = A/1$ and the reciprocal of B is $1/B$, this definition may
be restated as follows:

$$\frac{A}{B} = \frac{A}{1} \cdot \frac{1}{B} \qquad \text{or} \qquad \frac{c/d}{f/g} = \frac{c/d}{1} \cdot \frac{1}{f/g}$$

And this is consistent with the fact that every rational a/b is equal to
the product of $a/1$ by the reciprocal of $b/1$:

$$\frac{a}{b} = \frac{a}{1} \cdot \frac{1}{b}$$

This definition is clearly consistent, too, with the meaning of whole-
number division. Whether A and B are whole numbers *or* rationals,
$A \div B$ is the answer to the question "$A = B \times$?" (For example, $3 \div 2$
means $3 = 2 \times$? The answer is $3/2$, because $2 \times 3/2 = 3$. And $3/2 =$

$3 \times 1/2$, or *3 times the reciprocal of 2*.) In other words, the answer is always *A times the reciprocal of B*, or A/B: because (B times A/B) equals (A times B/B), which is equal to (A times *one*), which equals A. This means that every equation of the form $b \cdot x = a$ has a rational number solution, unless b is zero, even if the rationals a and b look like integers. The solution is $x = a/b$.

The properties of rationals provide the basis for understanding the principle of compensation for division. And in an interesting discussion of the identity element for multiplication, Reckzeh and Duncan show that it is one of two key concepts that together may be used to solve or analyze many different problems of everyday arithmetic.[8] (For convenience these authors refer to the multiplicative identity property as the "Law of One"; and this would be an appropriate way for children to say it.)

The other important concept used in such applications is this: There are many (indeed infinitely many) symbols for expressing any numerical quantity. (Materials for children often put it this way: "A number has many names.") For example, the following are all symbols for the same number: "one," $1/2 + 1/2$, 100%, 1.0, 4/4, $100 - 99$, and $3 \times 1/3$.

The five examples below, adapted from the Reckzeh-Duncan article, demonstrate the applicability of the Law of One to a variety of problems involving fractions or division. In each case the original number expression is first multiplied by an expression ("name") for the number "one." The selection of the appropriate name requires particular arithmetic understandings.

1. *Changing a fraction to smaller-size parts:*

$$\frac{2}{3} = \frac{2}{3} \times 1 = \frac{2}{3} \times \frac{2}{2} = \frac{4}{6}$$

The original number, 2/3, is multiplied by the appropriate name for "one" (2/2) in order to express it in terms of sixths. The choice of 2/2 is determined by dividing 6 (the desired denominator) by 3 (the original denominator).

2. *Changing a fraction to its largest-size parts* (in traditional language, "reducing to lowest terms"):

$$\frac{21}{35} = \frac{21}{35} \times 1 = \frac{21}{35} \times \frac{\frac{1}{7}}{\frac{1}{7}} = \frac{21 \times \frac{1}{7}}{35 \times \frac{1}{7}} = \frac{3}{5}$$

3. *Changing a fraction to its per-cent equivalent:*

$$\frac{1}{4} = \frac{1}{4} \times (100\%) = 25\%$$

4. *Changing a long division problem with a decimal divisor to one with a whole number divisor:* $2.31\overline{)7.3124}$. The conventional instructions for this kind of problem are to clear the divisor of the decimal point by moving it to the right as many places as necessary, and then to move the decimal point in the dividend an equal number of places to the right. The problem then becomes: $231\overline{)731.24}$. Using the Law of One, the procedure takes on meaning beyond its mechanical steps:

$$\frac{7.3124}{2.31} = \frac{7.3124}{2.31} \times \frac{100}{100} = \frac{731.24}{231}$$

5. *Dividing with fractions:*

$$\frac{2}{3} \div \frac{3}{4} = \frac{\dfrac{2}{3}}{\dfrac{3}{4}} \times \frac{12}{12} = \frac{\dfrac{2}{3} \times 12}{\dfrac{3}{4} \times 12} = \frac{8}{9}$$

The 12/12 name for "one" is the convenient choice for this solution, which depends only on finding a number, preferably the smallest, into which 3 and 4 (the two original denominators) divide evenly (traditionally known as "finding the least common denominator"). This analysis is instructive and does offer a valid method of solution, though it involves more steps than the "invert and multiply" process based on the definition of division. The authors relate that to the Law of One as follows:

$$\frac{\dfrac{2}{3}}{\dfrac{3}{4}} \times \frac{\dfrac{4}{3}}{\dfrac{4}{3}} = \frac{\dfrac{8}{9}}{1} = \frac{8}{9}$$

These methods of solution offer the student insights into meanings and processes (including the inversion method itself) which will later be important in working with algebraic equations.

There are many other instances where knowledge of the multiplicative identity can be useful. The search for new applications is a valuable experience for students, since this idea is a basic concept of modern mathematics structure.

IMPLICATIONS FOR EDUCATION

Perhaps the most significant implication regarding the basic mathematical properties discussed in this chapter is related to their having emerged *after* the development of standard algebraic and arithmetic symbolism.

The emphasis on structure that characterized the early nineteenth century led to the identification of the basic laws. They have become the pillars of arithmetic, and this structure has made possible a deeper understanding of number systems and served to provide clues to the development of other mathematical systems. Since the concepts themselves are generally considered suitable for elementary school curriculum and since they constitute a major contribution to mathematical thinking, it stands to reason that children's gains in learning about them can in some way parallel those of the mathematicians. The other principles and constructs discussed can also add much to young people's mathematical learning experience at appropriate levels.

The commutative law for addition ought to convey to teachers that requiring children to add numbers in a particular order—top to bottom or vice versa—is placing a limit on the mathematical freedom they deserve. In the example $(3+4+5+6)$ some children might note that the end numbers add up to 9, as do the two middle numbers, giving a total of 18. Others might first see the $6+4$ equaling 10 and then combine the 5 and 3 to give 8, and $10+8$ would give the correct sum, too. And some might experiment with different sets of four (or more) consecutive numbers to see what generalizations emerge.

Inviting children to look for helpful patterns and comfortable ways to solve problems can lead to a great variety of interesting ideas and possibilities. The sharing of these contributions of different youngsters can make the field of mathematics "come alive" in the classroom.

Asking students to think about the differences between the results of adding and multiplying proper fractions, as compared with the results for whole numbers or improper fractions, leads then to *expect* the *product* of two proper fractions to be *smaller* than *either*. And suggesting that students look for common meanings in sets of different but equal expressions can lead them to recognize, for example, that

$$\frac{1}{2} \times \frac{3}{4} = \frac{3}{4} \times \frac{1}{2} = \frac{3}{4} \div \frac{2}{1} = \frac{3}{4} \div 2$$

and that *all* of these mean—among other things—"one-half *of* three-fourths," or "three-fourths divided by two."

The use of the multiplicative identity in problems of varying complexity at the elementary school level, as illustrated by Reckzeh and Duncan, demonstrates a sense of continuity in this curriculum area. Other ways of providing for this much-needed element in the curriculum need to be identified and implemented.

For all of their grade school years, countless children have been told: "You can't subtract a larger number from a smaller one." Then, when they reached the ninth-grade algebra class, all at once they were faced with a contradiction to this deeply ingrained notion. Through reference to equality principles and negative numbers, one can clearly recognize the misinformation too often given to children. The inclusion of such ideas in young people's mathematics instruction adds one more important dimension to mathematics in terms of unifying patterns and operations. (The teacher who does not wish to become involved with negatives might tell children that *in arithmetic* a larger number cannot be subtracted from a smaller one, but that they will later learn about another meaning of subtraction that makes it always possible.)

The teacher who is aware of significant mathematical laws and principles can respond to children in ways that provide valuable and meaningful direction. If Tommy is trying to add $5+3$ and seems to be having some difficulty, Teacher A, who is unaware of the importance of commutativity in addition, may help him to work out his problem by having him count out five disks and then three more, and then find out how many he has altogether. Teacher B, whose background includes knowledge of this fundamental idea, might employ a specific pattern of questioning:

> Do you see another example on the page that looks a little like $5 + 3$? (Tommy has already done $3 + 5$ correctly.)

To establish that the numerals are the same and that only the order in which they appear is different, this teacher asks:

> What is the same about the two problems?
> What is different about them?
> Do you think the answers should be the same?
> Let's find out.

At this point, the process used by Teacher A might be employed, but Tommy is helped to use his counting materials for *both* combinations, $3+5$ and $5+3$. When it is clear to him that the answers are the same, Teacher B raises another question:

> Do you think this is true for just 3 and 5 or is it also true for other numbers like 2 and 6, 4 and 7?

Teacher B might then call the class's attention to the problem Tommy is working on and they might agree to try out many different combinations to see if there are any that do not work that way.

When sufficient experimentation has taken place, the class is asked to summarize their findings. If their response is something like "It doesn't matter which way (or in which order) you add numbers, you still get the same answer," they have grasped the essence of the law of commutation for addition. Labeling it *as such* is inconsequential, but having children select some easy way of referring to it is helpful.

Teacher B can add to the children's perception of the importance of this finding by saying that about a hundred or more years ago mathematicians made the same observation and they considered it a very important discovery in mathematics. That the mathematicians called this the law of commutation might eventually be mentioned. Students in the upper grades will, of course, be ready for this supplementary information initially.

Since the early nineteenth century, mathematicians have focused on analyzing and describing the existent mathematical systems. They have uncovered ideas, both simple and complex, upon which mathematics rests, and these in turn have given impetus to other mathematical developments to serve man.

Of the interdependency of observation and generalization, discovery and analysis, facts and systems, John Kemeny has said:

> In the historical development of mathematics, it is usually, though by no means always, the case that a certain body of mathematical facts is first discovered, and then one or more people perform the very important task of systematizing this information by specifying a minimal number of axioms and deriving the other facts from these. It is, therefore, clear both that some acquaintance with axiomatic mathematical systems is an important part of mathematical education, and that mathematics is something over and above mere development of axioms.[9]

As young people are helped to become acquainted with the ways in which scholars in the various disciplines approach the fields of knowledge, they will have a resource that profoundly affects their own learning. In the last analysis, however, the extent of a teacher's own knowledge of any field of study, and of the fields related to it, will in large part determine the quality of the direction he or she provides.

NINE

Sets

UNIFYING IDEAS

The idea of a set has always been a convenient way to classify objects in the physical environment. A child's earliest experiences involve sets of blocks or toys of some kind, and everyday life activities abound with the notion of set: a set of dishes, a collection of coins, a group of people, a class of children. For as long as there are records of recorded language (about twenty thousand years) collective nouns such as "flock" and "herd" appear. Current linguistic usage includes terms such as "bunch of grapes," "covey of partridges," and "pride of lions."

Although people have always used the idea of a set as a group of similar or related objects, the modern mathematical concept of a set is a relatively recent one. Mathematicians today find that this concept makes it possible to classify sets of numbers having different properties, such as the set of counting numbers or the set of fractional numbers. The development of these sophisticated and abstract concepts of set from man's simple observations of various kinds of groups has a most enlightening history.

SETS AND THE SCHOOL CURRICULUM

The "set" is the medium through which some contemporary mathematicians have approached the structure of mathematics. The set concept may be viewed as a unifying idea of higher mathematics, and only its simplest aspects can be approached in the elementary school. Unlike the areas of algebra, geometry, and measurement, which have long been generally accepted for elementary and/or secondary school study, the theory of sets was restricted to college and graduate classes in advanced mathematics prior to the mid-1950's.

An as idea very recently incorporated into elementary mathematics instruction, set theory has presented a problem to mathematicians and curriculum workers, who have deliberated as to where in the educational program it should be introduced. Some experts feel that work with sets should not be introduced before the fourth grade. Others recommend its inclusion in a kindergarten-through-twelfth-grade developmental program, and still others would introduce it only at the secondary school level.

An objection to introducing set concepts in the early grades has been that historically set theory was developed to deal with infinite processes, which are not part of elementary school work.

In contrast to this position is one holding that, regardless of the history of set theory, some of its basic concepts provide a solid foundation for understanding number as a property of a set, that the language of sets facilitates the precise formulation of ideas, and that work with sets should therefore be the starting point in mathematics instruction for children.

The highly complex nature of advanced mathematics developed in the language of sets, together with the new presence of "something about sets" in elementary curriculum, has caused teachers, and laymen too, to ask: What is set theory? What is so important about this idea that is has been made a central focus in recent curriculum development? The answers to these questions are not simple, and comprehension frequently depends upon some knowledge of the subject itself.

In actuality, the ideas regarding sets which are encompassed in current programs do not constitute set theory. Rather, only the vocabulary and basic operations of sets have been taken from advanced mathematics and made part of elementary education. This is part of the present educational emphasis on the introduction of fundamental concepts in mathematics as early in the curriculum as feasible.

Nearly every recently published textbook for teachers and children contains comprehensive instruction in elementary set language and operations. To present much of this kind of material here would be duplicating what is already widely available. This chapter does, however, include whatever explanations seem indicated in order to communicate ideas about the development of set theory and the relevance of some of its purposes and concepts to education.

First, its historical roots are explored in order to find what notions might meaningfully connect the past with the present for teachers, and consequently for children.

BEFORE SET THEORY

Before the ancient Greek civilizations, the mathematics of the more ancient cultures was almost totally utilitarian in nature. Mathematics was used for purely practical reasons, although there were indirect applications in matters of religious worship. For example, the Pyramids and the Stonehenge could not have been built without the use of complex mathematical concepts.

"It was the Greeks," as Zehna points out in *Sets with Applications*, "who first conceived of mathematics as a system of undefined terms, definitions, axioms, and postulates, with conclusions or theorems derived as logical consequences." [1]

From the time of ancient Greece to the early part of the seventeenth century, exceedingly little that was new was contributed to the science of mathematics. There were some developments in arithmetic and algebra, but these were essentially rules and mechanical procedures for simplifying certain mathematical operations.

Bell separates the history of mathematics development into three periods of unequal length: the remote period, extending from the earliest times of reliable recorded information to 1637; the middle period, from 1638 to 1800; and the recent period of modern mathematics as understood today, from 1801 to the present. He cites as bases for this division Descartes's *La géométrie* (1637), which begins the analytic phase of geometry, and Gauss's *Disquisitiones arithmeticae* (1801), which "marks the beginning of a new era of unprecedented inventiveness." [2]

The Calculus

Descartes's work provided the basis for the invention of the calculus, which has been termed "the most practical mathematics ever invented . . . the mathematics of movement." [3] This branch of mathematics was invented by Newton in England, and independently by Leibniz in Germany, in the latter half of the seventeenth century.

Detailed discussion of the calculus would be too far from the central purpose of this book. The information included here is intended only to communicate in a general way the pervasive importance of the calculus and the unprecedented impetus its invention supplied to mathematical theory.

Change is fundamental in every phase of life. The earth changes position as it rotates on its axis and as it moves around the sun; the molecules in the air are in constant motion; even rocks and steel blocks expand or shrink as temperatures change. Being continuous and usually uneven, change is difficult to analyze. For many centuries mathematicians struggled with the problem to little avail. The Greeks made some attempt to analyze change, instant by instant, by slicing curving lines into infinitesimally fine segments. Descartes made a great leap forward "when he conceived of the items in an equation as functions between *variables,* and most of all when he supplied a way to draw graph-pictures of *fluid* situations and relationships." [4] But it wasn't until the invention of the calculus that mathematical analysis of all movement and change became possible.

The calculus encompasses some of the most complex mathematical abstractions, yet is based on just a few simple ideas—function, approximation, rate of change, convergence, and integration. These ideas are explained and illustrated in an interesting and easily understandable fashion by David Bergamini and the editors of *Life* magazine in *Mathematics* (1963), pages 114–25. The comments that follow mention a few of the examples given there.

A *function* is usually described as a relationship between two variables, one being dependent upon the other. Weight is a function of calories, height a function of age, water pressure a function of depth, the amount of oxygen needed by an astronaut a function of his physical stress.

Rate of change means how much something is changing in relation to a change in something else. For example, *speed* is the measure of distance covered by a moving object in a given time (60 miles per hour, 80 feet per second, etc.); it is the rate of change in distance as a function of time. *Acceleration* is the measure of how much speed itself increases or decreases in a given time. Speeding up from 100 feet per second (100 ft./sec.) to 160 feet per second (160 ft./sec.) in 2 seconds, for example, is an average change of 30 feet per second in each second: 30 ft./sec./sec. (Thus acceleration, the rate of change in speed, is the rate of change in a rate of change!) Refining such *average* rates of change over measurable intervals down to the rate of change at a given *point* in space or time is one of the important operations of calculus. It is called *differentiation.*

Approximation, using smaller and smaller intervals of change, is a concept basic to this process of finding the exact rate of change taking place at a given point (as for example the acceleration of a rocket a certain number of seconds after liftoff). In the process, the differences between things (the changes taking place as a variable *approaches* the desired point) eventually become and remain so close to zero that it makes *no* difference.

Convergence in general refers to the diminishing difference between things that get ever closer and closer together; and in calculus a concept of "convergence to a limit" is used to assign definite values to unmeasurably small quantities, through approximations made finer and finer until they converge, in effect, to a point. A classic example of convergence is shown on pages 122–23 of the Bergamini book. This is a 206-figure decimal expansion of pi (π), a number which is the ratio of a circle's circumference to its diameter. The value of pi has, in fact, been carried to many more than 206 decimal places (no one has reached an end), and each successive expansion is a better approximation. This means that a mathematician may come as close to the true value of pi as he wishes (if he has time).

Integration in calculus is a process through which totals are found by "stuffing curves with rectangles." This means that the "area under a curve" (which cannot be determined by an algebraic formula) is theoretically filled with smaller and smaller rectangles of known area until the area *not* covered by rectangles approaches zero. An architectural illustration of integration would be finding the area of a wall under a curved roof.

"Once calculus was invented," says Bergamini, "mathematicians could treat a moving object as a point tracing a path through space and, by 'stopping the action,' calculate the object's speed and acceleration at a specific instant. The mathematics of motion became a fundamental scientific tool." Using this tool, Newton worked out the laws of motion and gravitation—"the fundamental laws of physics which explain why the solar system acts as it does, or why any moving object reacts as it does to outside forces like gravity, the tension of a spring, or the push of a man's hand." [5] And on the basis of Newton's work, scientists subsequently have been able to identify and analyze the three fundamental forces in nature: gravitation, magnetism, and atomic energy.

Other Developments

In the eighteenth and nineteenth centuries there was considerable extension of the work of Descartes, Newton, and Leibniz. The development of *structural analysis* of mathematics emerged; the concept of *function* was developed as one basic to all mathematics; and a definitive departure from intuitivism toward *abstraction* in mathematical reasoning took place.

Examples of the application and value of structural analysis as it has been applied in the field of mathematics would be of interest only to those with advanced preparation in pure mathematics. What should be said here, however, has been said by Bell: that this direction in the progress of mathematics was characterized by a move "toward ever greater generality and more refined abstraction which distinguished much mathematics of the recent period from nearly all that preceded

1840. Structure, in a sense to be noted and described, was the final outcome of this accelerated progression from the particular to the general." [6] The treatment of numbers as sets of elements—systems and subsystems with some distinctive properties and some common ones—is discussed in Chapter Eight, and illustrated in rudimentary representations of underlying mathematical structures.

This statement of Zehna's substantiates the importance of the concept of function and its relation to set theory.

> One of the most important concepts in the field of analysis is that of function, by which we intuitively mean a relationship between two variable quantities. Indeed, this one notion became so important that it is difficult to imagine any contemporary mathematics that does not employ the notion in one form or another. As a matter of fact, functions began to appear in so many separate branches of mathematics that each branch appeared to have its own definition. A single concept unifying these related ideas did not come about until the advent of set theory. [7]

Of necessity, the above material sketches only a few highlights in mathematical progress. The formulations of Descartes, Newton, and Leibniz had shortcomings that were remedied in later years. Nevertheless their contributions—analytic geometry and calculus—stand as the foundation of modern mathematics.

STARTING FROM INFINITY

The concept of sets is one of the most significant mathematical ideas of recent times, that is, since the 1880's. The significance of this concept was not immediately recognized even by such an eminently gifted mathematician as Gauss, who was violently repelled by the mere idea of infinity—a major starting point of set theory.

Since the time of the Greeks, philosophers and mathematicians have wrestled with problems involving infinite quantities. Galileo recognized that both the number of whole numbers and the number of even numbers were infinite. However, he questioned which of these two series of numbers was larger. By putting them into one-to-one correspondence, it was clear that there was always a number in the first series to correspond with a number in the second series, and vice versa. It seemed, however, that the series containing all the whole numbers should be larger than the series containing only the even numbers. [8] A logical thought!

The conclusion reached by many prominent mathematicians—Galileo, Leibniz, Gauss—was that infinite series could not be compared, that the idea was incomprehensible and inappropriate to the field of mathematics. The Greeks, as a matter of fact, had relegated this idea to theology.

It was in the late nineteenth century that Georg Cantor, a German mathematician, was successful in a significant attempt to deal with endless quantities.* He knew of course that the numbers or objects in an infinite series cannot be counted. But Cantor perceived and articulated another very simple and vitally important notion: If there is a one-to-one correspondence between the objects of any two series, then the two series have the same number of objects; counting the objects is not necessary in order to know this. For example, if a group of children each eating an ice cream cone is observed at a picnic, one need not count the children or the ice cream cones to know that there is the same number of each.

For another example, note that the series of whole numbers

$$1 \quad 2 \quad 3 \quad 4 \quad 5 \quad 6 \quad 7 \ldots$$

and the series of even numbers

$$2 \quad 4 \quad 6 \quad 8 \quad 10 \quad 12 \quad 14 \ldots$$

are related in such a way that every number in one series corresponds to just one number in the other series.

"Cantor's greatness," Kline says, "lies in his perception of the one-to-one correspondence principle and in his courage to pursue its consequences. *If two infinite classes can be put into one-to-one correspondence then*, according to Cantor, *they have the same number of objects in them.*" [9]

Cantor used the Hebrew letter *aleph* ($\aleph$) to represent the number of objects in an infinite collection, and a subscript to refer to the particular kind of endlessness. "Aleph-null" ($\aleph_0$) designates the number of objects in an infinite series that can be put into one-to-one correspondence with the natural numbers. It is called a transfinite number. (Not every infinite series can be put into one-to-one correspondence with the natural numbers; subscripts "one" and "two" have been used, and others are likely to be used in the future, to designate different types of endlessness.)

Kline explains that whereas it is theoretically possible to count a billion billion objects, so is it possible to put an infinite collection into one-to-one correspondence with numbers; the quantity of aleph-null,

* For a translation of Cantor's work with a detailed historical survey by Philip Jourdain, see Georg Cantor, *Contributions to the Founding of the Theory of Transfinite Numbers,* unaltered reprint of first published translation in 1915.

therefore, is as definite and valuable a fact as the quantity of a billion billion.[10]

Cantor's solution to Galileo's difficulty regarding the collection of whole numbers and the collection of even numbers was that both contained aleph-null objects, even though one collection was contained within the other. That the two collections are in one-to-one correspondence was the basis for his thinking. At a later time, an "infinite set" was defined, interestingly, as one that can be put into one-to-one correspondence with a part of itself, whereas a finite set cannot be.[11]

Kline, referring to the fact that modes of thought which had served for finite collections were not applicable to understanding infinite collections, makes this comment:

> It was the failure of mathematicians before Cantor's time to understand that they must abandon some habitual ways of thinking about quantity that kept them from developing the subject of infinite numbers.[12]

Cantor's work was not well received at first by many mathematicians, although some reacted positively "because the theory provided proof of the existence of transcendental numbers." [13] As applications of his theory to analysis and geometry became evident, his work gained acceptance. Around the turn of the century, a number of antinomies, or paradoxes, were found in Cantor's original work which caused many mathematicians to reconsider its worth.* Some of these antinomies still remain unsolved, but the usefulness of Cantor's theory was eventually established, and there ensued interest in a general theory of abstract sets in which his ideas appeared in greatly extended form.

BASIC CONCERNS AND CONCEPTS

Quine defines set theory as the mathematical theory of classes, but defers to Zarmelo's paper of 1908 as to its primary purposes:

> Set theory is that branch of mathematics whose task is to investigate the fundamental notions of number, of order, and of function in their original simplicity, and to develop thereby the logical foundations of all arithmetic and analysis.[14]

The word "set" is commonly used to mean a distinguishable collection of things or ideas. It is synonymous in that sense with "aggregate," "collection," "class," and "group"; with French *ensemble* and German *Menge*.

Mathematicians treat "set" and "member of a set" (or "element of a

---

* For a detailed systematic investigation of antinomies in Cantor's work see A. Fraenkel and Y. Bar-Hillel, *Foundations of Set Theory* (1958).

set") as undefined terms, holding that one must start from certain self-evident concepts and axiomatic conditions and proceed to define and prove other things in terms of these. However, any *particular* sets (as well as any operations applied to them) must be *clearly* defined so that logical conclusions can be drawn about them with certainty.

Cantor's own concept of the term "set" is quoted by Stoll: "A *set* S is any collection of definite, distinguishable objects of our intuition or of our intellect to be conceived as a whole. The objects are called the elements or members of S." [15] Of this statement, Stoll writes:

> The essential point of Cantor's concept is that a collection of objects is to be regarded as a single entity (to be conceived as a whole). The transfer of attention from individual objects as entities is commonplace, as evidenced by the presence in our language of such words as "bunch," "covey," "pride," "flock." [16]

In further analysis, Stoll explains that the phrase "objects of our intuition or of our intellect" permits extensive latitude in the selection of objects which may be part of a set. For mathematical applications, he comments, such entities as points, lines, numbers, and sets of numbers are selected. The freedom of choice would include sets whose elements cannot be explicitly shown—for example, infinite sets such as the set of all prime numbers, but also sets which have "the same degree of intangibility as any infinite set," such as the set of all books ever written. ("The magnitude eludes comprehension to the same degree as does that of an infinite set.")[17]

By "distinguishable" and "definite," Stoll says, Cantor referred to these requirements: (1) that it be possible to determine whether any particular pair of objects are different or the same; and (2) that if given a set and an object, it must be possible to determine whether the object is or is not a member of the set. "The implication is that a set is completely determined by its members." [18]

And this means, again, that although the word "set" itself needs no definition, any *particular* set referred to must be *exactly* defined by specifying or describing or exhibiting all of its members in a way that clearly distinguishes them from nonmembers.

ELEMENTARY APPLICATIONS

A booklet entitled *Sets, Sentences, and Operations* (1960), by Johnson and Glenn, is among the few materials available which relate the application of elementary set concepts to their theoretical framework, using a variety of problems with relevance to students' everyday experience. A sample problem from this excellent source is presented on pages 135–37.

Explanations follow here for the most basic symbols and terms used in elementary work with sets.

1. Brackets (or braces) are used to group the members of a set.
   EXAMPLE:
   $A = [1,2,3,4,5]$ is translated: "A is the set whose members are the first five counting numbers."

2. $n(A)$ is translated: "the number of members in set A."
   EXAMPLE:
   For set A above, $n(A) = 5$.

3. *Set.* A specific set is a well-defined collection of objects or ideas.

4. *Subset.* A set which is part of another set.
   EXAMPLE:
   $[1,3,5]$ is a subset of set A above.

5. The set of all subsets which can be formed from a set is called the *power set* of the original set. This idea has many applications in the mathematics of chance or probability, where the number of subsets tells the number of different ways events may occur.

6. *Union.* The union of two sets is the set of all elements belonging to one set or the other or both. (It is one of the two main operations on sets; the other is *intersection.*) Defined as applying to two sets at a time, it is called a binary operation. Just as, in arithmetic, an operation on two numbers gives another number (e.g., $3+4=7$), so an operation on two sets results in another set. The symbol for union is $\cup$, differing from U, which is used to represent the *universal set*, the set which consists of all the elements under consideration at a given time.
   EXAMPLE:
   $A = [\text{Mary, Jane, Tom}]$
   $B = [\text{Bob, Jane, Sue}]$
   $A \cup B = [\text{Mary, Jane, Tom, Bob, Sue}]$

7. *Intersection.* The intersection of two sets is the set that contains the members which are common to both sets. The symbol for intersection is $\cap$.
   EXAMPLE:
   The intersection of set A and set B of the example in 6 above would be as follows:
   $A \cap B = [\text{Jane}]$

8. *Venn diagrams.* Venn diagrams are very helpful in showing pictorially how sets are related. They are named for the English scholar who devised them, John Venn (1834–1923). Following are examples of sets and diagrams representing them:

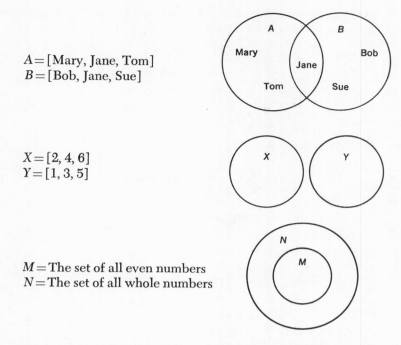

$A = [\text{Mary, Jane, Tom}]$
$B = [\text{Bob, Jane, Sue}]$

$X = [2, 4, 6]$
$Y = [1, 3, 5]$

$M =$ The set of all even numbers
$N =$ The set of all whole numbers

By using labels, colored lines, and shadings for different regions of such diagrams, relationships and the results of various operations may be made readily visible. For instance, in the diagram of sets A and B above, the overlapped area containing "Jane" would be shaded to show $A \cap B$.

A Sample Problem *

In a certain school there are 21 students in a mathematics course, 17 in physics, and 10 in advanced history. Of these, there are 12 students taking both mathematics and physics, 6 taking both mathematics and history, and 5 taking both physics and history; but these figures include 2 students who take all three subjects. If the three classes are combined for a field trip, accommodations will have to be secured for how many different students?

Let X be the set of all students taking mathematics, Y the set of all students taking physics, and Z the set of all students taking history. Since there are students taking all combinations of the three subjects, the three sets intersect. Then $X \cap Y$ represents the set of students taking both mathematics and physics, $X \cap Z$ the set of students taking both mathematics and history, $Y \cap Z$ the set of students taking both physics and history, $X \cap Y \cap Z$ the set of students taking all three subjects, and $X \cup Y \cup Z$ the total set of students under consideration.

Look now at the Venn diagram in Figure 16.

Region G represents the students who take mathematics, physics, and history.

$$n(G) = n(X \cap Y \cap Z)$$
$$= 2$$

Region F represents those who take physics and history, but no mathematics.

$$n(F) = n(X \cap Z) - n(G)$$
$$= 5 - 2$$
$$= 3$$

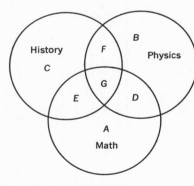

Figure 16

Region E represents those who take mathematics and history, but no physics.

$$n(E) = n(X \cap Z) - n(G)$$
$$= 6 - 2$$
$$= 4$$

Region D represents those who take physics and mathematics, but no history.

$$n(D) = n(X \cap Y) - n(G)$$
$$= 12 - 2$$
$$= 10$$

Region C represents those who take history, but no mathematics or physics.

$$n(C) = n(Z) - [n(F) + n(G) + n(E)]$$
$$= 10 - (3 + 2 + 4)$$
$$= 1$$

Region B represents those who take physics, but no mathematics or history.

$$n(B) = n(Y) - [n(F) + n(G) + n(D)]$$
$$= 17 - (3 + 2 + 10)$$
$$= 2$$

Region A represents those who take mathematics, but no physics or history.

$$n(A) = n(X) - [n(D) + n(E) + n(G)]$$
$$= 21 - (10 + 4 + 2)$$
$$= 5$$

The total number of different students, $n(X \cup Y \cup Z) = n(A) + n(B) + n(C) + n(D) + n(E) + n(F) + n(G) = 5 + 2 + 1 + 10 + 4 + 3 + 2 = 27$, so we need accommodations for 27 students.

Figure 17 shows the number of students in each region. Now we also know how many students have each combination of courses.

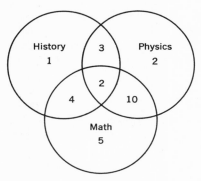

This is the way sets can be used to find the answers to many questions about groups of persons or events.

Figure 17

IMPLICATIONS FOR EDUCATION

How much of the historical background of set theory development can be dealt with in elementary or intermediate school remains open to question. Perhaps somewhere in the grades the simple ideas related to the development of the set concept can be discussed with children. Even in the very early grades, when children are first learning about the concept of number, a teacher might spark a discussion by asking: "How many numbers do you think there are?" Through further questioning and discussion the children might learn that a long time ago there were people who wondered how many numbers there were. These people reasoned that *no matter how large a number* they could think of, they could always say *that number and one more,* and so they came to understand that numbers can go on and on forever—there is no end. The same questions might be raised about the odd and even numbers, with the same reasoning applied.

The question of whether there are as many odd or even numbers as the odd and even numbers put together does not seem too advanced to have students in the upper grades consider. There seems to be no logical reason not to connect this question with the dilemma of mathematicians before Cantor's time. And inasmuch as young people today do many set problems involving *one-to-one correspondence*, not to associate this idea with a great mathematician's solution to a perplexing problem of long standing seems to place an unwarranted limit on their knowledge and understanding.

The language of sets places fundamental emphasis on the *clear classification* of information, and Zarmelo's view of the purposes of set theory affirms this emphasis, extending it to include the *logical processing* of information.*

That effective classification and processing of information is of vital concern in education today is evidenced by the nature of recent studies that have focused on cognitive development. One such study, by Hilda Taba, classified three levels of cognitive tasks: (1) grouping and labeling, (2) interpreting information and making inferences, and (3) predicting consequences and explaining new phenomena.[19]

Problems requiring the use of elementary set theory may require the student to operate on all three levels of Taba's classification. For example, in the sample problem on pages 135–37 the first two levels are involved in reaching the solution. Once it is determined that accommodations are needed for twenty-seven students, a variety of alternatives for meeting this need and the consequences of each alternative might be considered, thus involving the third cognitive level.

Whereas the problems in the average arithmetic textbook may involve these cognitive tasks, in general they do not call for an organized approach emphasizing the classification and processing of information, nor do they invite students to contemplate alternatives and consequences.

The knowledge explosion of this century has led to a growing concern on the part of educators for organizing the curriculum in ways that help children to order and process their information.

Since the idea of "sets" is basic to most new mathematics programs, and since work with sets begins in some instances as early as kindergarten, the importance of *continuity* in the development of this concept is unquestionable. "When abstract ideas or strategic concepts are set forth as the threads of continuity in a curriculum, the design of the curriculum differs greatly from that of a topic-centered curriculum."[20]

---

* For a timely comment on certain difficulties to be overcome in forming and communicating clear ideas, see Howard Levi's explanation of why set language is used in his mathematics: in *Foundations of Geometry and Trigonometry* (1960), p. 2.

Alice Miel is referring here to the opportunities for widening and deepening one's understanding of key concepts.

Ideas related to set theory—the purposes served today by classification of information, the questions people of earlier times raised, their problems, their needs, and ways of meeting these—comprise a strategic concept which ought to be a continuing thread in the study of elementary mathematics.

Appendix

Professional Bulletins With Descriptions of Mathematics Projects

ACEI (Association for Childhood Education International). *New Directions in Mathematics.* Washington, D.C.: The Association, 1965. 70 pp.

ASCD (Association for Supervision and Curriculum Development, NEA). *New Curriculum Developments.* Washington, D.C.: The Association, 1965. 106 pp.

————. *Using Current Curriculum Developments.* Washington, D.C.: The Association, 1963. 118 pp.

Deans, Edwina. *Elementary School Mathematics: New Directions.* Washington, D.C.: U. S. Department of Health, Education and Welfare, Office of Education, 1963. 116 pp.

Fraser, Dorothy M. *Current Curriculum Studies in Academic Subjects.* Washington, D.C.: National Education Association, 1962. 102 pp.

Goodlad, John I. *School Curriculum Reform.* New York: The Fund for the Advancement of Education, 1964. 95 pp.

NCTM (National Council of Teachers of Mathematics). *An Analysis of New Mathematics Programs.* Washington, D.C.: The Council, 1963. 68 pp.

————. *The Revolution in School Mathematics.* Washington, D.C.: The Council, 1961. 90 pp.

Scott, Lloyd. *Trends in Elementary School Mathematics.* Chicago: Rand McNally and Company, 1966. 215 pp.

Notes

Chapter One. *Introduction*

1. Augustus De Morgan, *Arithmetical Books: From the Invention of Printing to the Present Time* (1847), p. xxvii.
2. See for instance NCTM's 1959 Yearbook, *The Growth of Mathematical Ideas, Grades K-12*, pp. 480-98.
3. Peter L. Spencer and Marguerite Brydegaard, *Building Mathematical Concepts in the Elementary School* (1952), p. 268.
4. *Goals for School Mathematics: The Report of The Cambridge Conference on School Mathematics* (1963), p. 19.

Introduction to Part I

1. NCTM, *The Revolution in School Mathematics* (1961), p. 1.

Chapter Two. *The Movement*

1. Philip H. Phenix, "The Disciplines as Curriculum Content," in *Curriculum Crossroads*, ed. A. Harry Passow (1962), p. 65.
2. Philip H. Phenix, "Key Concepts and the Crisis in Learning," *Teachers College Record*, 58, No. 3 (December, 1956), 143.
3. Philip H. Phenix, *Philosophy of Education* (1958), p. 298.
4. Jerome S. Bruner, *The Process of Education* (1960), p. 7.
5. *Ibid.*, p. 25.
6. NCTM, *The Revolution in School Mathematics* (1961), pp. 1-2.
7. *Ibid.*, p. 2.
8. *Ibid.*, p. 4.
9. *Ibid.*, p. 4.

10. Dorothy M. Fraser, *Current Curriculum Studies in Academic Subjects* (1962), p. 27.

11. William Wooton, *SMSG: The Making of a Curriculum* (1965), pp. 11, 12-13.

12. Patrick Suppes, "Sets and Numbers" (1963), p. 2.

13. NCTM, *An Analysis of New Mathematics Programs* (1963), p. 10. Quoted as the purpose of the project in a statement prepared for this publication by the GCMP Research Staff.

Chapter Three. *Six Programs*

1. Educational Research Council of Greater Cleveland, *Greater Cleveland Mathematics Program: A Descriptive Outline* (1964), Introductory page.

2. *Ibid.*, p. 2.

3. Robert B. Davis, *A Modern Mathematics Program as It Pertains to the Interrelationship of Mathematical Content, Teaching Methods and Classroom Atmosphere* (1965), p. 20.

4. Robert B. Davis, *The Madison Project—A Brief Introduction to Material and Activities* (1965), pp. 2-7.

5. *Ibid.*, pp. 8-12.

6. Paul C. Rosenbloom, "A Leap Ahead in School Mathematics," in *Science and Mathematics: Countdown for Elementary Schools* (1959), pp. 24-31.

7. Paul C. Rosenbloom, "The Minnesota Mathematics and Science Teaching Project," *Journal of Research in Science Teaching*, I, No. 3 (1963), 276.

8. SMSG, *Information Memorandum* (1963), p. 6.

9. *Ibid.*, p. 1.

10. Patrick Suppes and Shirley Hill, "Set Theory in the Primary Grades," *Mathematics Teachers Journal*, XIII, No. 2 (April 1963), 46.

11. MINNEMAST, *Unit 6: Symmetry* (1963), p. VI-9.

12. Robert B. Davis, *Discovery in Mathematics: A Text for Teachers* (1964), p. 8.

13. H. Van Engen, "Twentieth Century Mathematics for the Elementary School," *The Arithmetic Teacher*, VI, No. 2 (March, 1959), 71, 72.

14. Frances Minor, "A Child Goes Forth: Ideas Invite Involvement," in *Individualizing Instruction* (1964), pp. 67-68.

Introduction to Part II

1. G. Heppel, "The Use of History in Teaching Mathematics," *Nature*, 48, No. 1227 (1893), p. 16. Abstract of a paper read before the Association for the Improvement of Geometrical Teaching.

2. Herbert Spencer, *Education: Intellectual, Moral, Physical* (1892), p. 91.

Chapter Four. *Numeration*

1. NCTM, *Enrichment Mathematics for the Grades* (1963), p. 41.

2. R. Osborn, M. DeVault, C. C. Boyd, and W. R. Houston, *Extending Mathematics Understanding* (1961), p. 129.

3. Tobias Dantzig, *Number: The Language of Science* (1954), p. 12.

4. Florian Cajori, *A History of Elementary Mathematics* (1896), p. 1.

5. David E. Smith and Jekuthiel Ginsburg, *Numbers and Numerals* (1937), p. 4.

6. *Ibid.*, p. 6.

7. David E. Smith, *History of Mathematics* (1923-25), II, 26.

8. Smith and Ginsburg, *Numbers and Numerals*, p. 7.

9. Smith and Ginsburg, *Numbers and Numerals*, pp. 8-10.

10. Herta Taussig Freitag and Arthur H. Freitag, *The Number Story* (1960), p. 3.

11. Francis J. Mueller, *Arithmetic: Its Structure and Concepts* (1956), p. 6.

12. Florian Cajori, *A History of Elementary Mathematics*, rev. ed. (1937), pp. 3-5.

13. *Ibid.*, p. 10.

14. Cajori, *History of Elementary Mathematics* (1937), p. 11.

15. *Ibid.*, p. 13.

16. Dantzig, *Number*, p. 34.

17. *Ibid.*, pp. 31-32.

18. Morris Kline, *Mathematics: A Cultural Approach* (1962), p. 56.

19. Dantzig, *Number*, p. 35.

20. *Ibid.*, p. 30.

Chapter Five. *Measurement*

1. J. Houston Banks, *Learning and Teaching Arithmetic* (1959), p. 342.

2. C. West Churchman and Philburn Ratoosh, *Measurement: Definitions and Theories* (1959), p. vi.

3. Osborn et al., *Extending Mathematics Understanding*, p. 156.

4. Mueller, *Arithmetic* (1956), pp. 230-31; and Osborn et al., *Extending Mathematics Understanding*, pp. 156-57.

5. NCTM, *Growth of Mathematical Ideas*, p. 193.

6. SUNY, *Geometry and Measurement* (1965), p. 17.

7. William L. Schaaf, *Basic Concepts of Elementary Mathematics* (1965), p. 292.

8. J. E. Williams, H. C. Metcalfe, F. E. Trinklein, and R. W. Lefler, *Modern Physics* (1968), p. 21.

9. *Ibid.*

10. Mueller, *Arithmetic* (1956), p. 232.

11. Isaac Asimov, *Realm of Measure* (1960), p. 4.

12. *Ibid.*, p. 6.

13. Richard W. Copeland, *Mathematics and the Elementary Teacher* (1966), p. 272.

14. Osborn et al., *Extending Mathematics Understanding*, p. 162.

15. Quoted in Mueller, *Arithmetic* (1956), p. 233.

16. Cajori, *History of Elementary Mathematics* (1937), p. 170.

17. Martin P. Nilsson, "Calendar," *Encyclopaedia Britannica* (1952 ed.), IV, 573.

18. See Kline, *Mathematics: A Cultural Approach,* pp. 12-14.

19. Lewis Van Hagen Judson, "Measurement," *Encyclopaedia Britannica* (1952 ed.), XV, 134.

20. Mueller, *Arithmetic* (1956), p. 235.

21. *Ibid.,* p. 239.

22. *Ibid.*

23. U.S. National Bureau of Standards of the Commerce Department, "A Metric America—A Decision Whose Time Has Come," an 88-page distillation of a twelve-volume report (1971).

24. David Rappaport, *Understanding and Teaching Elementary School Mathematics* (1966), p. 161.

Chapter Six. *Geometry*

1. Osborn et al., *Extending Mathematics Understanding,* pp. 141-42.

2. Irvin H. Brune, "Geometry in the Grades," in *Enrichment Mathematics for the Grades* (1963), p. 136.

3. Lancelot Hogben, *The Wonderful World of Mathematics* (1955), p. 12.

4. *Ibid.,* p. 13.

5. *Ibid.,* p. 14.

6. James Gow, *A Short History of Greek Mathematics* (1884), pp. 125-26.

7. Hogben, *Wonderful World of Mathematics,* p. 16.

8. *Ibid.,* pp. 16-17.

9. *Ibid.,* p. 17.

10. Mueller, *Arithmetic* (1964), p. 327.

11. Smith, *History of Mathematics,* II, 270.

12. Gow, *Short History of Greek Mathematics,* p. 126.

13. *Ibid.,* p. 124.

14. Cajori, *History of Elementary Mathematics* (1896), p. 44.

15. Philip E. B. Jourdain, *The Nature of Mathematics* (1919), p. 21.

16. Cajori, *History of Elementary Mathematics* (1896), p. 45.

17. *Ibid.*

18. Gow, *Short History of Greek Mathematics,* pp. 129-31.

19. Cajori, *History of Elementary Mathematics* (1896), p. 46.

20. Gow, *Short History of Greek Mathematics,* p. 131.

21. Cajori, *History of Elementary Mathematics* (1896), p. 43.

22. Smith, *History of Mathematics,* II, 271.

23. Cajori, *History of Elementary Mathematics* (1896), pp. 89-91.

24. Smith, *History of Mathematics,* II, 271.

25. Cajori, *History of Elementary Mathematics* (1896), pp. 46-48.

26. *Ibid.,* p. 48.

27. Gow, *Short History of Greek Mathematics,* p. 141.

28. Florian Cajori, "History of Geometry," *Encyclopaedia Britannica* (1952 ed.), X, 178.

29. Smith, *History of Mathematics,* I, 72.

30. Cajori, *History of Elementary Mathematics* (1896), p. 49

31. Gow, *Short History of Greek Mathematics,* p. 149.
32. Smith, *History of Mathematics,* I, 75.
33. Gow, *Short History of Greek Mathematics,* p. 135.
34. Morris Kline, *Mathematics and the Physical World* (1959), pp. 27-28.
35. *Ibid.,* p. 29.
36. *Ibid.,* p. 42.
37. *Ibid.,* pp. 42-43.
38. *Ibid.,* p. 43.
39. *Ibid.,* p. 45.
40. *Ibid.,* p. 45.
41. *Ibid.,* pp. 48-49.
42. Quoted in Gow, *Short History of Greek Mathematics,* p. 135.
43. Jourdain, *The Nature of Mathematics,* p. 25.
44. Gow, *Short History of Greek Mathematics,* p. 174.
45. Smith, *History of Mathematics,* I, 90.
46. Gow, *Short History of Greek Mathematics,* p. 176.
47. Thomas L. Heath, *A Manual of Greek Mathematics* (1931), p. 175.
48. *Ibid.*
49. Gow, *Short History of Greek Mathematics,* p. 176.
50. *Ibid.,* p. 175.
51. Cajori, "History of Geometry," p. 179.
52. Gow, *Short History of Greek Mathematics,* p. 137.
53. Smith, *History of Mathematics,* I, 104.
54. Cajori, "History of Geometry," p. 179.
55. Smith, *History of Mathematics,* I, 106.
56. John Wesley Young, *Lectures on Fundamental Concepts of Algebra and Geometry* (1911), p. 9.
57. *Ibid.,* p. 12.
58. Kline, *Mathematics and the Physical World,* p. 89.
59. Heath, *Manual of Greek Mathematics,* p. 280.
60. Smith, *History of Mathematics,* I, 68.
61. Alfred North Whitehead, *An Introduction to Mathematics* (1948), p. 82.
62. Smith, *History of Mathematics,* II, 316-17.
63. *Ibid.,* p. 321.
64. *Ibid.*
65. Morris Kline, *Mathematics in Western Culture* (1953), pp. 164-65.
66. John Stuart Mill, *An Examination of Sir William Hamilton's Philosophy* (1867), p. 601.
67. Cajori, *History of Elementary Mathematics* (1896), p. 43.
68. Kline, *Mathematics and the Physical World,* p. 74.
69. *Ibid.,* p. 89.

Chapter Seven. *Algebra*

1. Kline, *Mathematics and the Physical World,* p. 42.
2. Dantzig, *Number,* p. 30.

3. Ibid., p. 76.
4. Smith, *History of Mathematics*, II, 379.
5. Dantzig, *Number*, p. 77.
6. Smith, *History of Mathematics*, II, 378.
7. *Ibid.*, p. 381.
8. *Ibid.*, I, 48; and Dantzig, *Number*, p. 77.
9. Dantzig, *Number*, p. 77.
10. Smith, *History of Mathematics*, I, 133-34, 157-59; II, 379.
11. *Ibid.*, I, 134.
12. *Ibid.*, pp. 157-59.
13. E. T. Bell, *The Development of Mathematics* (1945), p. 18.
14. *Ibid.*, p. 97.
15. *Ibid.*, p. 95.
16. Dantzig, *Number*, p. 30.
17. Bell, *Development of Mathematics*, pp. 95-96.
18. *Ibid.*, p. 96.
19. Smith, *History of Mathematics*, II, 386, 392.
20. Dantzig, *Number*, p. 76.
21. Smith, *History of Mathematics*, I, 170; II, 388.
22. Bell, *Development of Mathematics*, pp. 99-100.
23. Smith, *History of Mathematics*, I, 275-78.
24. Smith, *History of Mathematics*, I, 177; and Dantzig, *Number*, pp. 82-83.
25. Smith, *History of Mathematics*, I, 227.
26. *Ibid.*, pp. 269-73.
27. David Eugene Smith, "Algebra," *Encyclopaedia Britannica* (1952 ed.), I, 603.
28. Kline, *Mathematics and the Physical World*, p. 59.
29. Smith, *History of Mathematics*, II, 384; I, 300.
30. *Ibid.*, I, 297-99.
31. Cajori, *History of Elementary Mathematics* (1896), pp. 225-26.
32. Smith, *History of Mathematics*, I, 300-01; II, 386.
33. Kline, *Mathematics and the Physical World*, pp. 59-60.
34. Smith, *History of Mathematics*, I, 388-89; II, 413.
35. Cajori, *History of Elementary Mathematics* (1896), p. 234.
36. *Ibid.*
37. *Ibid.*, p. 232.
38. *Ibid.*, p. 227.
39. *Ibid.*, pp. 232-33.
40. *Ibid.*, p. 233.
41. Kline, *Mathematics and the Physical World*, p. 52.
42. *Ibid.*
43. Cajori, *History of Elementary Mathematics* (1896), p. 233.
44. *Ibid.*
45. *Ibid.*, pp. 234-35.
46. *Ibid.*, p. 235.
47. Smith, *History of Mathematics*, II, 395.

48. *Ibid.*
49. *Ibid.*, p. 402.
50. *Ibid.*, p. 398.
51. *Ibid.*
52. Cajori, *History of Mathematical Notations*, I, 77.
53. Smith, *History of Mathematics*, II, 405.
54. Cajori, *History of Mathematical Notations*, I, 80-81.
55. Quoted in Smith, *History of Mathematics*, II, 411.
56. *Ibid.*, pp. 411-12.
57. Cajori, *History of Mathematical Notations*, I, 297-99.
58. *Ibid.*, pp. 298-301.
59. *Ibid.*, pp. 302-03.
60. *Ibid.*, pp. 305-06.
61. Bertrand Russell, *The Autobiography of Bertrand Russell, 1872-1914* (1967), p. 40.
62. Augustus De Morgan, *Arithmetical Books: From the Invention of Printing to the Present Time* (1847), p. xxiii.
63. Smith, *History of Mathematics*, II, 393-94.
64. *Ibid.*, p. 385.
65. Dantzig, *Number*, p. 82.
66. Kline, *Mathematics and the Physical World*, p. 60.
67. *Ibid.*, p. 68.
68. *Ibid.*

Chapter Eight. *Structure*

1. Florian Cajori, *History of Mathematics*, 2d ed. (1919), p. 273.
2. E. T. Bell, "History of Mathematics," *Encyclopaedia Britannica* (1952 ed.), XV, 87B.
3. Cajori, *History of Mathematics*, p. 273; and Smith, *History of Mathematics*, II, 395.
4. Howard Eves and Caroll V. Newsom, *An Introduction to the Foundations and Fundamental Concepts of Mathematics* (1958), p. 119.
5. Bruce E. Meserve, "Implications for the Mathematics Curriculum," in *Insights into Modern Mathematics* (23rd Yearbook, NCTM, 1957), pp. 406, 407.
6. Irving Adler, *The New Mathematics* (1958), pp. 9-10.
7. Mueller, *Arithmetic* (1956), p. 71.
8. John K. Reckzeh and Ernest R. Duncan, "E Pluribus Unum—A Brief Discussion on the 'Law of One,' " *The Arithmetic Teacher*, VIII, No. 8 (December 1961), 413-15.
9. John G. Kemeny, "Report to the International Congress of Mathematicians," *The Mathematics Teacher*, LVI, No. 2 (February 1963), 76.

Chapter Nine. *Sets*

1. Peter W. Zehna, *Sets with Applications* (1966), p. 4.
2. Bell, *Development of Mathematics*, pp. 14-15.

3. David Bergamini et al., *Mathematics* (1963), p. 88.

4. *Ibid.*, p. 105.

5. *Ibid.*

6. Bell, *Development of Mathematics*, p. 245.

7. Zehna, *Sets with Applications*, p. 6.

8. Kline, *Mathematics in Western Culture*, pp. 395-96.

9. *Ibid.*, p. 398.

10. *Ibid.*, p. 399.

11. *Ibid.*, p. 400.

12. *Ibid.*

13. Robert R. Stoll, *Set Theory and Logic* (1961), p. 1.

14. Willard Van Orman Quine, *Set Theory and Its Logic* (1963), p. 4.

15. Stoll, *Set Theory and Logic*, p. 2.

16. *Ibid.*

17. *Ibid.*, p. 3.

18. *Ibid.*

19. Hilda Taba, *Thinking in Elementary School Children* (1964), p. 152.

20. Alice Miel, *Sequence in Learning—Fact or Fiction* (1967), p. 2.

Bibliography

ACEI (Association for Childhood Education International). *New Directions in Mathematics.* Washington, D.C.: The Association, 1965.

Adler, Irving. *The New Mathematics.* 1958. Reprint. New York: New American Library (Signet Books), n.d.

"Algebra." *Encyclopaedia Britannica* (1st ed.), I, 79.

Asimov, Isaac. *Realm of Measure.* Boston: Houghton Mifflin Company, 1960.

————. *Realm of Numbers.* Boston: Houghton Mifflin Company, 1959.

Ball, W. W. Rouse. *A Primer of the History of Mathemtics.* 2d ed. 1903. Reprint. London: Macmillan and Company, 1927.

————. *A Short Account of the History of Mathematics.* 4th ed. 1908. Reprint. London: Macmillan and Company, 1919.

Banks, J. Houston. *Learning and Teaching Arithmetic.* Boston: Allyn and Bacon, 1959.

Bell, E. T. *The Development of Mathematics.* 2d ed. New York: McGraw-Hill Book Company, 1945.

————. "History of Mathematics." *Encyclopaedia Britannica* (1952 ed.), XV, 87B.

————. *Men of Mathematics.* London: Victor Gollancz, 1937.

Bergamini, David, and the Editors of *Life. Mathematics.* Life Science Library Edition. New York: Time Incorporated, 1963.

Bezuska, Stanley, S. J. *Co-op Unit Study Program.* Boston College Mathematical Series. Boston: Boston College Mathematics Institute Press, 1960.

Brune, Irvin H. "Geometry in the Grades." *Enrichment Mathematics for the Grades.* Twenty-seventh Yearbook of the National Council of Teachers of Mathematics. Washington, D. C.: The Council, 1963.

Bruner, Jerome S. *The Process of Education.* Cambridge, Mass.: Harvard University Press, 1960.

Cajori, Florian. *A History of Elementary Mathematics*. New York: Macmillan Company, 1896.

————. *A History of Elementary Mathematics*. Rev. ed. New York: Macmillan Company, 1937.

————. *A History of Mathematical Notations*. 2 vols. Chicago: Open Court Publishing Company, 1928-29.

————. *History of Mathematics*. 2d ed. New York: Macmillan Company, 1919.

————. "History of Geometry." *Encyclopaedia Britannica* (1952 ed.), X, 178-79.

Cantor, Georg. *Contributions to the Founding of the Theory of Transfinite Numbers*. 1915. Reprint. New York: Dover Publications, n.d.

Churchman, C. West, and Ratoosh, Philburn. *Measurement: Definitions and Theories*. New York: John Wiley and Sons, 1959.

Copeland, Richard W. *Mathematics and the Elementary Teacher*. Philadelphia: W. B. Saunders Company, 1966.

Dantzig, Tobias. *Number: The Language of Science*. New York: Macmillan Company, 1954.

Davis, Robert B. *A Modern Mathematics Program As It Pertains to the Interrelationship of Mathematical Content, Teaching Methods, and Classroom Atmosphere*. Cooperative Research Project No. D-093. Washington, D.C.: Department of Health, Education and Welfare, U.S. Office of Education, 1965.

————. *Discovery in Mathematics: A Text for Teachers*. Madison Project material. Palo Alto, Calif.: Addison-Wesley Publishing Company, 1964.

————. *Discovery in Mathematics: Student Discussion Guide*. Madison Project material. Palo Alto, Calif.: Addison-Wesley Publishing Company, 1964.

————. *The Changing Curriculum: Mathematics*. Washington, D.C.: Association for Supervision and Curriculum Development, 1967.

————. *The Madison Project: A Brief Introduction to Materials and Activities*. Syracuse, N.Y.: The Project, 1965.

Deans, Edwina. *Elementary School Mathematics: New Directions*. Washington, D.C.: U.S. Department of Health, Education and Welfare, Office of Education, 1963.

De Morgan, Augustus. *Arithmetical Books: From the Invention of Printing to the Present Time*. London: Taylor and Walton, 1847.

Educational Policies Commission. *The Contemporary Challenge to American Education*. Washington, D.C.: National Education Association, 1958.

Educational Research Council of Greater Cleveland. *Greater Cleveland Mathematics Program: A Descriptive Outline*. Cleveland: The Council, 1964. 9 pp.

————. *Greater Cleveland Mathematics Program: Teachers' Guide*. Books K, 1-6. Chicago: Science Research Associates, 1961-62.

Eicholz, Robert E.; Martin, Emerson, Jr.; Brumfiel, Charles F.; and Shanks, Merrill E. *Elementary School Mathematics*. Teachers' edition. Books K,

1-6. Ball State University Experimental Mathematics Project. Reading, Mass.: Addison-Wesley Publishing Company, 1964-65.

Eves, Howard, and Newsom, Carroll V. *An Introduction to the Foundations and Fundamental Concepts of Mathematics.* New York: Rinehart, 1958.

Fehr, Howard F.; Bunt, Lucas N. H.; and Grossman, George. *An Introduction to Sets, Probability, and Hypothesis Testing.* Boston: D. C. Heath and Company, 1964.

Fraenkel, Abraham A., and Bar-Hillel, Yehoshua. *Foundations of Set Theory.* Amsterdam: North Holland Publishing Company, 1958.

Fraser, Dorothy M. *Current Curriculum Studies in Academic Subjects.* Washington, D.C.: National Education Association, 1962.

Freitag, Herta Taussig, and Freitag, Arthur H. *The Number Story.* Washington, D.C.: National Council of Teachers of Mathematics, 1960.

Goodlad, John I. *School Curriculum Reform.* New York: The Fund for the Advancement of Education, 1964.

Gow, James. *A Short History of Greek Mathematics.* London: Cambridge University Press, 1884.

Heath, Sir Thomas. *A History of Greek Mathematics.* 2 vols. London: Oxford University Press, 1921.

————. *A Manual of Greek Mathematics.* Oxford: Clarendon Press, 1931.

Heppel, G. "The Use of History in Teaching Mathematics." *Nature,* 48, No. 1227 (1893), 16-18.

Hill, G. F. *The Development of Arabic Numerals in Europe.* London: Oxford University Press, 1915.

Hogben, Lancelot. *The Wonderful World of Mathematics.* New York: Garden City Books, 1955.

Johnson, Donavan A., and Glenn, William H. *Sets, Sentences, and Operations.* New York: McGraw-Hill Book Company, Webster Division, 1960.

Jourdain, Philip E. B. *The Nature of Mathematics.* Rev. ed. London: T. C. and E. C. Jack, 1919.

Judson, Lewis Van Hagen. "Measurement." *Encyclopaedia Britannica* (1952 ed.), XV, 134.

Kemeny, John G. "Report to the International Congress of Mathematicans." *Mathematics Teacher,* LVI, No. 2 (February 1963), 66-78.

Kline, Morris. *Mathematics: A Cultural Approach.* Reading, Mass.: Addison-Wesley Publishing Company, 1962.

————. *Mathematics and the Physical World.* New York: Thomas Y. Crowell Company, 1959.

————. *Mathematics in Western Culture.* New York: Oxford University Press, 1953.

Larsen, Harold D. *The Story of Time.* White Plains, N.Y.: Row, Peterson and Company, 1956.

Levi, Howard. *Foundations of Geometry and Trigonometry.* Englewood Cliffs, New Jersey: Prentice-Hall, 1960.

MacLane, Saunders. "Algebra." *Insights into Modern Mathematics.* Twenty-third Yearbook of the National Council of Teachers of Mathematics. Washington, D.C.: The Council, 1957.

"Mathematics." *Encyclopaedia Britannica* (1st ed.), III, 30.

Meserve, Bruce E. "Implications for the Mathematics Curriculum." *Insights into Modern Mathematics.* Twenty-third Yearbook of the National Council of Teachers of Mathematics. Washington, D.C.: The Council, 1957.

Miel, Alice. *Sequence in Learning—Fact or Fiction.* Elementary Instructional Service Report 282-08810. Washington, D.C.: Department of Elementary-Kindergarten-Nursery Education, NEA, 1967.

Mill, John Stuart. *An Examination of Sir William Hamilton's Philosophy.* 3d ed. London: Longmans, Green, Reader, and Dyer, 1867.

MINNEMAST (Minnesota Mathematics and Science Teaching Project). *Mathematics for the Elementary School.* Units 1-9, 11-24. For use in grades K-4. Minneapolis: University of Minnesota, 1963-64.

Minor, Frances. "A Child Goes Forth: Ideas Invite Involvement." *Individualizing Instruction.* 1964 Yearbook of the Association for Supervision and Curriculum Development. Washington, D.C.: The Association, 1964.

Mueller, Francis J. *Arithmetic: Its Structure and Concepts.* Englewood Cliffs, New Jersey: Prentice-Hall, 1956.

———. *Arithmetic: Its Structure and Concepts.* 2d ed. Englewood Cliffs, New Jersey: Prentice-Hall, 1964.

NCTM (National Council of Teachers of Mathematics). *An Analysis of New Mathematics Programs.* Washington, D. C.: The Council, 1963.

———. *Enrichment Mathematics for the Grades.* Twenty-seventh Yearbook. Washington, D.C.: The Council, 1963.

———. *The Growth of Mathematical Ideas, Grades K-12.* Twenty-fourth Yearbook. Washington, D.C.: The Council, 1959.

———. *The Revolution in School Mathematics.* Washington, D.C.: The Council, 1961.

Neugebauer, O. *The Exact Sciences in Antiquity.* Princeton, N.J.: Princeton University Press, 1952.

Nilsson, Martin P. "Calendar." *Encyclopaedia Britannica* (1952 ed.), IV, 573.

Osborn, Roger; De Vault, M. Vere; Boyd, Claude C.; and Houston, W. Robert. *Extending Mathematics Understanding.* Columbus, Ohio: Charles E. Merrill Books, 1961.

Partridge, Eric. *Origins: A Short Etymological Dictionary of Modern English.* New York: Macmillan Company, 1958.

Phenix, Philip H. "The Disciplines as Curriculum Content." *Curriculum Crossroads.* A. Harry Passow, editor. New York: Teachers College Press, 1962.

———. "Key Concepts and the Crisis in Learning." *Teachers College Record,* 58, No. 3 (December 1956), 137-43.

———. *Philosophy of Education.* New York: Henry Holt and Company, 1958.

Quine, Willard Van Orman. *Set Theory and Its Logic.* Cambridge, Mass. Harvard University Press, Belknap Press, 1963.

Rappaport, David. *Understanding and Teaching Elementary School Mathematics*. New York: John Wiley and Sons, 1966.

Reckzeh, John K., and Duncan, Ernest. "E Pluribus Unum—A Brief Discussion on the 'Law of One.' " *The Arithmetic Teacher*, VIII, No. 8 (December 1961), pp. 413-15.

Rosenbloom, Paul C. "A Leap Ahead in School Mathematics." *Science and Mathematics: Countdown for Elementary Schools*. Proceedings of a symposium held in Oklahoma City, December 4, 1959. Oklahoma City: Frontiers of Science Foundation of Oklahoma, 1959.

————. "The Minnesota Mathematics and Science Teaching Project." *Journal of Research in Science Teaching*, I, No. 3 (1963), 276-80.

————, ed. *Modern Viewpoints in the Curriculum*. New York: McGraw-Hill Book Company, 1964.

Russell, Bertrand. *The Autobiography of Bertrand Russell, 1872-1914*. Boston: Little, Brown and Company, 1967.

Schaaf, William L. *Basic Concepts of Elementary Mathematics*. 2d ed. New York: John Wiley and Sons, 1965.

Simon, Leonard, and Bendick, Jeanne. *The Day the Numbers Disappeared*. New York: McGraw-Hill Book Company, Whittlesey House, 1963.

Smith, David Eugene. "Algebra." *Encyclopaedia Britannica* (1952 ed.), I, 603.

————. *History of Mathematics*. 2 Vols. New York: Dover Publications, 1923-25.

———— and Ginsburg, Jekuthiel. *Numbers and Numerals*. Washington, D.C.: National Council of Teachers of Mathematics, 1937.

———— and Karpinski, Louis Charles. *The Hindu-Arabic Numerals*. Boston: Ginn and Company Publishers, 1911.

SMSG (School Mathematics Study Group). *Information Memorandum*. Stanford, Calif.: The Project, 1963.

————. *Mathematics for the Elementary School. Teachers' Commentary*. Books K, 1-6. New Haven and London: Yale University Press, 1965.

Spencer, Herbert. *Education: Intellecutual, Moral, Physical*. New York: E. L. Kellogg and Company, 1892.

Spencer, Peter L., and Brydegaard, Marguerite. *Building Mathematical Concepts in the Elementary School*. New York: Holt, Rinehart and Winston, 1952.

Stoll, Robert R. *Set Theory and Logic*. San Francisco: W. H. Freeman and Company, 1961.

SUNY (University of the State of New York, State Education Department, Bureau of Elementary Curriculum Development). *Geometry and Measurement*. Albany: The University, 1965.

Suppes, Patrick. *Axiomatic Set Theory*. Princeton, N.J.: D. Van Nostrand Company, 1960.

————. "Sets and Numbers." An Experimental Project in the Teaching of Elementary School Mathematics, 1962-63. Stanford, Calif.: Institute for

Mathematical Studies in the Social Sciences, January 1963. (Mimeographed.)

——. *Sets and Numbers Series.* Teachers' edition. Books K, 1-6. Stanford University Sets and Numbers Project. New York: L. W. Singer Company, 1966.

—— and Hill, Shirley. "Set Theory in the Primary Grades." *Mathematics Teacher,* XIII, No. 2 (April 1963), 46-53.

Taba, Hilda. *Thinking in Elementary School Children.* San Francisco: San Francisco State College, 1964.

U.S. National Bureau of Standards of the Commerce Department. "A Metric America—A Decision Whose Time Has Come." A distillation of a 12-volume report. Washington, D.C.: The Bureau, 1971, 88 pp.

Van Engen, H. "Twentieth Century Mathematics for the Elementary School." *Arithmetic Teacher,* VI, No. 2 (March 1959), 71-76.

Whitehead, Alfred North. *An Introduction to Mathematics.* New York: Oxford University Press, 1948.

Williams, John E.; Metcalfe, H. Clark; Trinklein, Frederick E.; and Lefler, Ralph W. *Modern Physics.* Teachers' edition. New York: Holt, Rinehart and Winston, 1968.

Wooton, William. *SMSG: The Making of a Curriculum.* New Haven: Yale University Press, 1965.

Young, John Wesley. *Lectures on Fundamental Concepts of Algebra and Geometry.* New York: Macmillan Company, 1911.

Zehna, Peter W. *Sets with Applications.* Boston: Allyn and Bacon, 1966.

Index

157